BIG IDEAS
MATH®
Modeling Real Life
Grade 7

Student Journal

- Review & Refresh

- Exploration Journal

- Practice Worksheets

- Notetaking with Vocabulary

- Self-Assessments

- Exploration Manipulatives

BIG IDEAS
LEARNING®
Erie, Pennsylvania

About the Student Journal

Review & Refresh

The Review & Refresh provides students the opportunity to practice prior skills necessary to move forward.

Exploration Journal

The Exploration pages correspond to the Exploration in the Pupil Edition. Here students have room to show their work and record their answers.

Practice Worksheets

Each section of the Pupil Edition has an additional practice on the key concepts taught in the lesson.

Notetaking with Vocabulary

The student-friendly notetaking component is designed to be a reference for key vocabulary from the lesson. There is room for students to add definition to their words and take notes about key ideas.

Self-Assessment

For every lesson, students can rate their understanding of the learning target and success criteria.

Exploration Manipulatives

Manipulatives needed for the explorations are included in the back of the Student Journal.

Printed in the United States

ISBN 13: 978-1-64208-125-1

3456789-22 21 20 19 18

Contents

Contents

Contents

Contents

Contents

Contents

Contents

Name_____ Date_____

Chapter 1 Review & Refresh

Simplify the expression. Explain each step.

1. $2 + (5 + y)$

2. $(c + 1) + 9$

3. $(2.3 + n) + 1.4$

4. $7 + (d + 5)$

5. $(t + 3) + 0$

6. $0 + (g + 4)$

Review & Refresh (continued)

Evaluate the expression.

7. $\frac{1}{8} + \frac{1}{9}$

8. $\frac{2}{3} + \frac{9}{10}$

9. $\frac{7}{12} - \frac{1}{4}$

10. $\frac{6}{7} - \frac{4}{5}$

11. You have 8 cups of sugar. A recipe calls for $\frac{2}{3}$ cup of sugar. Another recipe calls for $\frac{1}{4}$ cup of sugar. How much sugar do you have left after making the recipes?

Name_____ Date_____

Rational Numbers
For use with Exploration 1.1

Learning Target: Understand absolute values and ordering of rational numbers.

Success Criteria:
- I can graph rational numbers on a number line.
- I can find the absolute value of a rational number.
- I can use a number line to compare rational numbers.

1 **EXPLORATION:** Using a Number Line

Work with a partner. Make a number line on the floor. Include both negative numbers and positive numbers.

a. Stand on an integer. Then have your partner stand on the opposite of the integer. How far are each of you from 0? What do you call the distance between a number and 0 on a number line?

b. Stand on a rational number that is not an integer. Then have your partner stand on any other number. Which number is greater? How do you know?

1.1   **Rational Numbers** (continued)

c. Stand on any number other than 0 on the number line. Can your partner stand on a number that is:

greater than your number and farther from 0?

greater than your number and closer to 0?

less than your number and the same distance from 0?

less than your number and farther from 0?

For each case in which it is not possible to stand on a number as directed, explain why it is not possible. In each of the other cases, how can you decide where your partner can stand?

1.1 Notetaking with Vocabulary

Vocabulary:

Notes:

1.1 Self-Assessment

Use the scale below to rate your understanding of the learning target and the success criteria.

1	2	3	4
I do not understand.	I can do it with help.	I can do it on my own.	I can teach someone else.

	Rating	Date
1.1 Rational Numbers		
Learning Target: Understand absolute values and ordering of rational numbers.	1 2 3 4	
I can graph rational numbers on a number line.	1 2 3 4	
I can find the absolute value of a rational number.	1 2 3 4	
I can use a number line to compare rational numbers.	1 2 3 4	

1.1 Practice

Complete the statement using <, >, or =.

1. $|-23|$ ____ 23

2. $|-142|$ ____ $|-157|$

3. $-|-78|$ ____ 52

4. You and your friend are swimming against the current. You move forward 15 feet. Your friend is not a strong swimmer, so he moves back 6 feet.

   a. Write each amount as an integer.

   b. Write each amount as the distance swam.

Order the values from least to greatest.

5. $14, |-25|, -|-34|, 28, |0|$

6. $|-16|, 10, |25|, -16, |-43|$

7. The boiling point of a liquid is the temperature at which the vapor pressure of the liquid equals the environmental pressure surrounding the liquid.

Substance	Hydrogen	Oxygen	Iodine	Phosphorus
Boiling Point (°C)	−253	−183	184	280

   a. Which substance in the table has the highest boiling point? Explain.

   b. Is the boiling point of oxygen or iodine closer to 0°C? Explain.

8. You are riding a rollercoaster.

   a. Your velocity is 13 feet per second. Are you moving up or moving down?

   b. What is your speed in part (a)? Give the units.

   c. Your velocity is −17 feet per second. Are you moving up or moving down?

   d. What is your speed in part (c)? Give the units.

9. There is one integer for which there does not exist another integer with the same absolute value. What is that integer?

Determine whether the statement is *true* or *false*. Explain your reasoning.

10. The absolute value of 3 above par is the same as the absolute value of 3 below par.

11. If $x < 0$, then $|x| < x$.

Name_____ Date _____

1.2 Adding Integers
For use with Exploration 1.2

Learning Target: Find sums of integers.

Success Criteria:
- I can explain how to model addition of integers on a number line.
- I can find sums of integers by reasoning about absolute values.
- I can explain why the sum of a number and its opposite is 0.

---

1 EXPLORATION: Using Integer Counters to Find Sums

Work with a partner. You can use the integer counters shown at the right to find sums of integers.

a. How can you use integer counters to model a sum? a sum that equals 0?

b. What expression is being modeled below? What is the value of the sum?

1.2 **Adding Integers** (continued)

c. Use integer counters to complete the table.

Expression	Type of Sum	Sum	Sum: Positive, Negative, or Zero
$-3 + 2$	Integers with different sign		
$-4 + (-3)$			
$5 + (-3)$			
$7 + (-7)$			
$2 + 4$			
$-6 + (-2)$			
$-5 + 9$			
$15 + (-9)$			
$-10 + 10$			
$-6 + (-6)$			
$13 + (-13)$			

d. How can you tell whether the sum of two integers is *positive*, *negative*, or *zero*?

e. Write rules for adding (i) two integers with the same sign, (ii) two integers with different signs, and (iii) two opposite integers.

1.2 Notetaking with Vocabulary

Vocabulary:

Notes:

1.2 Self-Assessment

Use the scale below to rate your understanding of the learning target and the success criteria.

1	**2**	**3**	**4**
I do not understand.	I can do it with help.	I can do it on my own.	I can teach someone else.

	Rating	Date
1.2 Adding Integers		
Learning Target: Find sums of integers.	1 2 3 4	
I can explain how to model addition of integers on a number line.	1 2 3 4	
I can find sums of integers by reasoning about absolute values.	1 2 3 4	
I can explain why the sum of a number and its opposite is 0.	1 2 3 4	

Name _____ Date _____

1.2 Practice

1. The elevation of your plot of land is 2 feet below sea level. You add 7 feet of dirt to your land. What is the new elevation of your land?

Tell how the Commutative and Associative Properties of Addition can help you find the sum using mental math. Then find the sum.

2. $18 + (-25) + (-18)$ 3. $-22 + 45 + (-8)$ 4. $28 + (-12) + 4$

Find the sum.

5. $(-63) + 81 + 0$ 6. $101 + (-51) + (-36)$ 7. $(-117) + 125 + (-67)$

Describe the location of the sum, relative to p, on a number line.

8. $p + 5$ 9. $p + (-2)$ 10. $p + (-q)$

Use mental math to solve the equation.

11. $n + (-20) = 5$ 12. $c + (-71) = 0$ 13. $-30 + k = -110$

14. Write three integers that do not all have the same sign that have a sum of -20. Write three integers that do not all have the same sign that have a sum of 10.

15. The temperature at 6 A.M. is $-12°F$. During the next twelve hours, the temperature increases $25°F$. During the following 5 hours, the temperature decreases $23°F$. What is the temperature at 11 P.M.?

16. Complete the magic square so that each row and column has a magic sum of 0. Use integers from -9 to 9, without repeating an integer.

9		-3
	2	

17. Consider the integers p and q. Describe all of the possible values of p and q for each circumstance. Justify your answers.

   a. $|p| + |-q| = 0$ b. $|p| + |-q| < 0$ c. $|p| + |-q| > 0$

1.3 Adding Rational Numbers
For use with Exploration 1.3

Learning Target: Find sums of rational numbers.

Success Criteria:
- I can explain how to model addition of rational numbers on a number line.
- I can find sums of rational numbers by reasoning about absolute values.
- I can use properties of addition to efficiently add rational numbers.

1 EXPLORATION: Adding Rational Numbers

Work with a partner.

a. Choose a unit fraction to represent the space between the tick marks on each number line. What addition expressions are being modeled? What are the sums?

1.3 Adding Rational Numbers (continued)

b. Do the rules for adding integers apply to all rational numbers? Explain your reasoning.

c. You have used the following properties to add integers. Do these properties apply to all rational numbers? Explain your reasoning.

Commutative Property of Addition

Associative Property of Addition

Additive Inverse Property

1.3 Notetaking with Vocabulary

Vocabulary:

Notes:

1.3 Self-Assessment

Use the scale below to rate your understanding of the learning target and the success criteria.

1	2	3	4
I do not understand.	I can do it with help.	I can do it on my own.	I can teach someone else.

	Rating	Date
1.3 Adding Rational Numbers		
Learning Target: Find sums of rational numbers.	1 2 3 4	
I can explain how to model addition of rational numbers on a number line.	1 2 3 4	
I can find sums of rational numbers by reasoning about absolute values.	1 2 3 4	
I can use properties of addition to efficiently add rational numbers.	1 2 3 4	

1.3 Practice

1. Describe and correct the error in finding the sum.

$$\times \ 2\tfrac{5}{6} + \left(-\tfrac{8}{15}\right) = \tfrac{13}{6} + \left(-\tfrac{8}{15}\right) = \tfrac{65+(-16)}{30} = \tfrac{49}{30} = 1\tfrac{19}{30}$$

Evaluate the expression when $x = -\tfrac{1}{5}$ and $y = \tfrac{3}{4}$.

2. $x + (-y)$ 3. $4x + y$ 4. $-|x| + y$

5. Your banking account is –$1.56. You deposit $10. What is your new balance?

6. You mow $\tfrac{1}{3}$ of the lawn. Your sister mows $\tfrac{2}{7}$ of the lawn. What fraction of the lawn is not mowed?

Find the sum. Write fractions in simplest form.

7. $1\tfrac{1}{4} + \left(-4\tfrac{1}{5}\right) + \left(-2\tfrac{3}{5}\right)$ 8. $-\tfrac{1}{3} + 2\tfrac{2}{9} + \left(-5\tfrac{2}{3}\right)$ 9. $-1.5 + (14.2) + 7.3$

10. When is the sum of two rational numbers with different signs positive?

11. The table at the right shows the amount of snowfall (in inches) for three months compared to the yearly average. Is the snowfall for the three-month period greater than or less than the yearly average? Explain.

December	January	February
$1\tfrac{2}{3}$	$-2\tfrac{1}{6}$	$2\tfrac{5}{6}$

12. The table below shows the weekly profits of a concession stand. What must the Week 5 profit be to break even over the 5-month period?

Week 1	Week 2	Week 3	Week 4	Week 5
2.4	–1.7	5.4	–3.75	

13. When is the sum of two positive decimal numbers an integer?

1.4 Subtracting Integers
For use with Exploration 1.4

Learning Target: Find differences of integers.

Success Criteria: • I can explain how subtracting integers is related to adding integers.
   • I can explain how to model subtraction of integers on a number line.
   • I can find differences of integers by reasoning about absolute values.

1 **EXPLORATION:** Using Integer Counters to Find Differences

Work with a partner.

   a. Use integer counters to find the following sum and difference. What do you notice?

$$4 + (-2) \qquad\qquad 4 - 2$$

   b. In part (a), you *removed* zero pairs to find the sums. How can you use integer counters and zero pairs to find $-3 - 1$?

1.4 **Subtracting Integers** (continued)

c. Use integer counters to complete the table.

Expression	Operation: Add or Subtract	Answer
4 – 2	Subtract 2	
4 + (–2)		
–3 – 1		
–3 + (–1)		
3 – 8		
3 + (–8)		
9 – 13		
9 + (–13)		
–6 – (–3)		
–6 + 3		
–5 – (–12)		
–5 + 12		

d. Write a general rule for subtracting integers.

Notetaking with Vocabulary

Vocabulary:

Notes:

 Self-Assessment

Use the scale below to rate your understanding of the learning target and the success criteria.

1	**2**	**3**	**4**
I do not understand.	I can do it with help.	I can do it on my own.	I can teach someone else.

	Rating	**Date**
1.4 Subtracting Integers		
Learning Target: Find differences of integers.	1 2 3 4	
I can explain how subtracting integers is related to adding integers.	1 2 3 4	
I can explain how to model subtraction of integers on a number line.	1 2 3 4	
I can find differences of integers by reasoning about absolute values.	1 2 3 4	

Big Ideas Math: Modeling Real Life Grade 7   **17**
Student Journal

Name _____ Date _____

1.4 Practice

1. A dolphin is at −28 feet. It swims up and jumps out of the water to a height of 8 feet. Find the vertical distance the dolphin travels. Justify your answer.

Evaluate the expression.

2. $0 - (-41) - 28$

3. $-51 - (-23) + (-16)$

4. $8 - (-103) - (-95)$

Tell how the Commutative and Associative Properties of Addition can help you evaluate the expression using mental math. Then evaluate the expression.

5. $-(-22) + 17 - 22$

6. $[-15 + (-31)] + 15$

7. $19 + (-19 - 24)$

8. The table shows the record monthly high and low temperatures in International Falls, Minnesota.

	Jan	Feb	Mar	Apr	May	Jun	Jul	Aug	Sep	Oct	Nov	Dec
High (°F)	48	58	76	93	95	99	98	95	95	88	73	57
Low (°F)	−46	−45	−38	−14	11	23	34	30	20	2	−32	−41

a. Find the range of temperatures for each month.

b. What are the all-time high and all-time low temperatures?

c. What is the range of the temperatures in part (b)?

Use mental math to solve the equation.

9. $c - (-15) = 38$

10. $-5 - k = -12$

11. $-25 - m = 28$

12. For what values of a and b is the statement $|a - b| = |a| - |b|$ false?

13. Write two different pairs of negative integers, x and y, that make the statement $x - y = 6$ true.

Describe the location of the difference, relative to p, on a number line.

14. $p - 3$

15. $p - (-5)$

16. $p - q$

17. Write two different triples of integers, x, y, and z, that meet the following conditions.

a. They do not all have the same sign and $x - y - z = 0$.

b. They all have the same sign and $(-x) + y - z = -17$

1.5 Subtracting Rational Numbers
For use with Exploration 1.5

Learning Target: Find differences of rational numbers and find distances between numbers on a number line.

Success Criteria:
- I can explain how to model subtraction of rational numbers on a number line.
- I can find differences of rational numbers by reasoning about absolute values.
- I can find distances between numbers on a number line.

---

1 EXPLORATION: Subtracting Rational Numbers

Work with a partner.

a. Choose a unit fraction to represent the space between the tick marks on each number line. What expressions involving subtraction are being modeled? What are the differences.?

b. Do the rules for subtracting integers apply to all rational numbers? Explain your reasoning?

c. You have used the commutative and associative properties to add integers. Do these properties apply in expressions involving subtraction? Explain your reasoning.

1.5 Subtracting Rational Numbers (continued)

2 EXPLORATION: Finding Distances on a Number Line

Work with a partner.

    a. Find the distance between 3 and −2 on a number line.

    b. The distance between 3 and 0 is the absolute value of 3, because $|3 - 0| = |3| = 3$. How can you use absolute values to find the distance between 3 and −2? Justify your answer.

    c. Choose any two rational numbers. Use your method in part (b) to find the distance between the numbers. Use a number line to check your answer.

Name_____ Date_____

1.5 Notetaking with Vocabulary

Vocabulary:

Notes:

1.5 Self-Assessment

Use the scale below to rate your understanding of the learning target and the success criteria.

1	2	3	4
I do not understand.	I can do it with help.	I can do it on my own.	I can teach someone else.

	Rating	Date
1.5 Subtracting Rational Numbers		
Learning Target: Find differences of rational numbers and find distances between numbers on a number line.	1 2 3 4	
I can explain how to model subtraction of rational numbers on a number line.	1 2 3 4	
I can find differences of rational numbers by reasoning about absolute values.	1 2 3 4	
I can find distances between numbers on a number line.	1 2 3 4	

1.5 Practice

Find the distance between the two numbers on a number line.

1. $-7\frac{1}{5}, -4\frac{2}{3}$

2. $-9.2, 4.5$

3. $-2, -3.7$

4. The largest orange in a bag has a circumference of $9\frac{5}{8}$ inches. The smallest orange has a circumference of $7\frac{13}{16}$ inches. Write the difference of the circumferences of the smallest orange and the largest orange. Then find the difference.

Evaluate the expression.

5. $\frac{5}{12} - \left(-3\frac{1}{4}\right) + \left(-6\frac{1}{2}\right) - 3$

6. $23.706 - (-82.31) - 130.641$

7. $-\frac{3}{8} - (-4.35)$

8. $-\frac{5}{18} - \left|-\frac{1}{6}\right| + \left(-\frac{7}{9}\right)$

9. Your bank account balance is $32.00. You make the following withdrawals, in the following order: $15.00, $7.41, $35.79, and $0.53. After each withdrawal that leaves a negative balance, the bank adds a $-$32.00 bank fee to your account. What is your new balance?

10. Fill in the blanks to make the solution correct.

$$3\frac{3}{4} - \boxed{}\frac{\boxed{}}{8} = 2$$

11. When is the difference of two mixed numbers an integer? Explain.

12. Points $A\left(5, \frac{2}{3}\right)$ and $B\left(5, 1\frac{1}{6}\right)$ lie in a coordinate plane.

   a. Find the distance between the points based on the x-coordinates. Interpret your answer.

   b. Find the distance between the points based on the y-coordinates.

   c. Write the expression for the difference of the y-coordinates, relative to point A.

   d. Write the expression for the difference of the y-coordinates, relative to point B.

   e. If the y-coordinate represents the number of bushels of apples picked, which of your answers, *part (c)* or *part (d)*, agrees with the statement "The number of bushels of apples picked is $\frac{1}{2}$ less than last year."?

Name_____ Date _____

Chapter Self-Assessment

Use the scale below to rate your understanding of the learning target and the success criteria.

1	**2**	**3**	**4**
I do not understand.	I can do it with help.	I can do it on my own.	I can teach someone else.

	Rating	Date
1.1 Rational Numbers		
Learning Target: Understand absolute values and ordering of rational numbers.	1 2 3 4	
I can graph rational numbers on a number line.	1 2 3 4	
I can find the absolute value of a rational number.	1 2 3 4	
I can use a number line to compare rational numbers.	1 2 3 4	
1.2 Adding Integers		
Learning Target: Find sums of integers.	1 2 3 4	
I can explain how to model addition of integers on a number line.	1 2 3 4	
I can find sums of integers by reasoning about absolute values.	1 2 3 4	
I can explain why the sum of a number and its opposite is 0.	1 2 3 4	
1.3 Adding Rational Numbers		
Learning Target: Find sums of rational numbers.	1 2 3 4	
I can explain how to model addition of rational numbers on a number line.	1 2 3 4	
I can find sums of rational numbers by reasoning about absolute values.	1 2 3 4	
I can use properties of addition to efficiently add rational numbers.	1 2 3 4	

Chapter 1 Chapter Self-Assessment (continued)

	Rating	Date
1.4 Subtracting Integers		
Learning Target: Find differences of integers.	1 2 3 4	
I can explain how subtracting integers is related to adding integers.	1 2 3 4	
I can explain how to model subtraction of integers on a number line.	1 2 3 4	
I can find differences of integers by reasoning about absolute values.	1 2 3 4	
1.5 Subtracting Rational Numbers		
Learning Target: Find differences of rational numbers and find distances between numbers on a number line.	1 2 3 4	
I can explain how to model subtraction of rational numbers on a number line.	1 2 3 4	
I can find differences of rational numbers by reasoning about absolute values.	1 2 3 4	
I can find distances between numbers on a number line.	1 2 3 4	

Chapter 2 **Review & Refresh**

Simplify the expression. Explain each step.

1. $10(7t)$

2. $8(4k)$

3. $13 \cdot 0 \cdot p$

4. $7 \cdot z \cdot 0$

5. $2.5 \cdot w \cdot 1$

6. $1 \cdot x \cdot 19$

Write the decimal as a fraction.

7. 0.26

8. 0.79

Write the fraction as a decimal.

9. $\dfrac{4}{10}$

10. $\dfrac{17}{20}$

Chapter 2 **Review & Refresh** (continued)

11. A quarterback completed 0.6 of his passes during a game. Write the decimal as a fraction.

Write the mixed number as an improper fraction.

12. $-3\frac{1}{5}$

13. $4\frac{3}{7}$

14. $8\frac{2}{3}$

15. $-10\frac{5}{6}$

Evaluate the expression.

16. $\frac{5}{9} \cdot \frac{1}{3}$

17. $\frac{8}{15} \cdot \frac{3}{4}$

18. $\frac{7}{8} \div \frac{11}{16}$

19. $\frac{3}{10} \div \frac{2}{5}$

Name_____ Date _____

2.1 Multiplying Integers
For use with Exploration 2.1

Learning Target: Find products of integers.

Success Criteria:
- I can explain the rules for multiplying integers.
- I can find products of integers with the same sign.
- I can find products of integers with different signs.

---

1 **EXPLORATION:** Understanding Products Involving Negative Integers

Work with a partner.

a. The number line and integer counters model the product $3 \cdot 2$. How can you find $3 \cdot (-2)$? Explain.

b. Use the tables to find $-3 \cdot 2$ and $-3 \cdot (-2)$. Explain your reasoning.

$2 \cdot 2 = 4$	
$1 \cdot 2 = 2$	
$0 \cdot 2 = 0$	
$-1 \cdot 2 = $ ___	
$-2 \cdot 2 = $ ___	
$-3 \cdot 2 = $ ___	

$-3 \cdot 3 = -9$	
$-3 \cdot 2 = -6$	
$-3 \cdot 1 = -3$	
$-3 \cdot 0 = $ ___	
$-3 \cdot -1 = $ ___	
$-3 \cdot -2 = $ ___	

2.1 **Multiplying Integers** (continued)

c. Complete the table. Then write general rules for multiplying (i) two
   integers with the same sign and (ii) two integers with different signs.

Expression	Type of Product	Product	Product: Positive or Negative
$3 \cdot 2$	Integers with the same sign		
$3 \cdot (-2)$			
$-3 \cdot 2$			
$-3 \cdot (-2)$			
$6 \cdot 3$			
$2 \cdot (-5)$			
$-6 \cdot 5$			
$-5 \cdot (-3)$			

2.1 Notetaking with Vocabulary

Vocabulary:

Notes:

2.1 Self-Assessment

Use the scale below to rate your understanding of the learning target and the success criteria.

1	2	3	4
I do not understand.	I can do it with help.	I can do it on my own.	I can teach someone else.

	Rating	Date
2.1 Multiplying Integers		
Learning Target: Find products of integers.	1 2 3 4	
I can explain the rules for multiplying integers.	1 2 3 4	
I can find products of integers with the same sign.	1 2 3 4	
I can find products of integers with different signs.	1 2 3 4	

2.1 Practice

1. The water in a pool evaporates at a rate of 16 gallons per week. What integer represents the change in the number of gallons of water in the pool after 24 weeks?

Evaluate the expression.

2. -12^2

3. $(-2)^3 \cdot (-3)^2$

4. $-9 \cdot 0 \cdot (-3)$

5. $-|-3| \cdot (-6)$

6. $11(-3) - (-2)(7)$

7. $-5 \cdot 8 - (-4)^3$

8. The gym offers a discount when more than one member of the family joins. The first member ($n = 0$) pays \$550 per year. The second member to join ($n = 1$) gets a discount of \$75 per year. The third member ($n = 2$) gets an additional \$75 discount. The price for the nth member is given by $550 + (-75n)$.

   a. What is the price for the fourth member to join ($n = 3$)?

   b. For a large family, is it possible that a member would join for free? If so, which member would it be? Explain your reasoning.

   c. Other than \$0, what is the lowest amount that a member would pay to join? Which member would it be? Explain your reasoning.

9. Two integers, a and b, have a product of -48.

   a. What is the greatest possible sum of a and b?

   b. Is it possible for a and b to have a sum of 13? If so, what are the integers?

   c. What is the least possible difference of a and b?

Tell whether the statement is *true* or *false*. Explain your reasoning.

10. The product of three negative integers is negative.

11. The product of four negative integers is negative.

12. The product of two negative integers and one positive integer is negative.

13. The product of one negative integer and two positive integers is negative.

14. If there is an odd number of negative integers, then the product will be negative.

Name_____ Date_____

2.2 Dividing Integers
For use with Exploration 2.2

Learning Target: Find quotients of integers.

Success Criteria:
- I can explain the rules for dividing integers.
- I can find quotients of integers with the same sign.
- I can find quotients of integers with different signs.

---

1 EXPLORATION: Understanding Quotients Involving Negative Integers

Work with a partner.

a. Discuss the relationship between multiplication and division with your partner.

b. Complete the table. Then write general rules for dividing (i) two integers with the same sign and (ii) two integers with different signs.

Expression	Type of Quotient	Quotient	Quotient: Positive, Negative, or Zero
$-15 \div 3$	Integers with different signs		
$12 \div (-6)$			
$10 \div (-2)$			
$-6 \div 2$			
$-12 \div (-12)$			
$-21 \div (-7)$			
$0 \div (-15)$			
$0 \div 4$			
$-5 \div 4$			
$5 \div (-4)$			

2.2 Dividing Integers (continued)

c. Find the values of $-\frac{8}{4}$, $\frac{-8}{4}$, and $\frac{8}{-4}$. What do you notice? Is it true for $-\frac{a}{b}$, $\frac{-a}{b}$, and $\frac{a}{-b}$ when a and b are integers? Explain.

d. Is every quotient of integers a rational number? Explain your reasoning.

2.2 Notetaking with Vocabulary

Vocabulary:

Notes:

2.2 Self-Assessment

Use the scale below to rate your understanding of the learning target and the success criteria.

1	*2*	*3*	*4*
I do not understand.	I can do it with help.	I can do it on my own.	I can teach someone else.

	Rating	Date
2.2 Dividing Integers		
Learning Target: Find quotients of integers.	1 2 3 4	
I can explain the rules for dividing integers.	1 2 3 4	
I can find quotients of integers with the same sign.	1 2 3 4	
I can find quotients of integers with different signs.	1 2 3 4	

2.2 Practice

Find the quotient, if possible.

1. $\dfrac{-144}{-9}$

2. $\dfrac{0}{25}$

3. $-15 \div (-15)$

4. $-82 \div 0$

5. $-96 \div 8$

6. $225 \div (-25)$

7. $\dfrac{-156}{3}$

8. $\dfrac{99}{-9}$

9. Your team catches 42 Mahi Mahi over 2 weeks. What is the average daily Mahi Mahi catch?

Evaluate the expression.

10. $(-68) \div (-4) + 5 \cdot (-3)$

11. $10 - 12^2 \div (-2)^3$

12. $-|-16| \div (-8) \cdot 5^2$

13. $\dfrac{3 + 7 \cdot (-3^2)}{-5}$

14. PI-Squared and Euler Circles are in a math competition consisting of 10 two-part questions. Both parts correct earns 5 points, one part correct earns 2 points, and no parts correct earns −1 point.

   a. What is the mean points per question for PI-Squared?

   b. What is the mean points per question for Euler Circle?

Team	Both	One	None
PI-Squared	4	2	4
Euler Circles	2	6	2

   c. Which team should win the competition? Explain your reasoning.

15. A 155-pound person burns about 500 calories per hour playing racquetball.

   a. One pound is equal to 3500 calories. How long will it take to burn 1 pound playing racquetball?

   b. How long will it take to burn 5 pounds playing racquetball? Explain your reasoning.

   c. If the person were to rest 5 minutes every 30 minutes of playing, how long would it take to burn 1 pound?

16. Find the next two numbers in the pattern $729, -243, 81, -27, \ldots.$ Explain your reasoning.

2.3 Converting Between Fractions and Decimals

For use with Exploration 2.3

Learning Target: Convert between different forms of rational numbers.

Success Criteria:
- I can explain the difference between terminating and repeating decimals.
- I can write fractions and mixed numbers as decimals.
- I can write decimals as fractions and mixed numbers.

1 EXPLORATION: Analyzing Denominators of Decimal Fractions

Work with a partner.

a. Write each decimal as a fraction or mixed number.

$$0.7 \qquad 1.29 \qquad 12.831 \qquad 0.0041$$

b. What do the factors of the denominators of the fractions you wrote have in common? Is this always true for decimal fractions?

2.3 **Converting Between Fractions and Decimals** (continued)

2 **EXPLORATION:** Exploring Decimal Representations

Work with a partner.

a. A fraction $\frac{a}{b}$ can be interpreted as $a \div b$. Use a calculator to convert each unit fraction to a decimal. Do some of the decimals look different than the others? Explain.

$$\frac{1}{2} \qquad \frac{1}{3} \qquad \frac{1}{4} \qquad \frac{1}{5}$$

$$\frac{1}{6} \qquad \frac{1}{7} \qquad \frac{1}{8}$$

$$\frac{1}{9} \qquad \frac{1}{10} \qquad \frac{1}{11} \qquad \frac{1}{12}$$

b. Compare and contrast the fractions in part (s) with the fractions you wrote in Exploration 1. What conclusions can you make?

c. Does every fraction have a decimal form that either *terminates* or *repeats*? Explain your reasoning.

2.3 Notetaking with Vocabulary

Vocabulary:

Notes:

2.3 Self-Assessment

Use the scale below to rate your understanding of the learning target and the success criteria.

1	2	3	4
I do not understand.	I can do it with help.	I can do it on my own.	I can teach someone else.

	Rating	Date
2.3 Converting Between Fractions and Decimals		
Learning Target: Convert between different forms of rational numbers.	1 2 3 4	
I can explain the difference between terminating and repeating decimals.	1 2 3 4	
I can write fractions and mixed numbers as decimals.	1 2 3 4	
I can write decimals as fractions and mixed numbers.	1 2 3 4	

2.3 Practice

Write the fraction or mixed number as a decimal.

1. $-5\frac{3}{40}$ **2.** $-\frac{3}{22}$ **3.** $4\frac{1}{15}$ **4.** $-9\frac{1}{9}$

Write the decimal as a fraction or mixed number in simplest form.

5. 0.68   **6.** 8.745   **7.** −9.98   **8.** −10.452

9. You caught a red snapper that is $8\frac{5}{12}$ inches long. Your friend caught a red snapper that is $8\frac{6}{13}$ inches long. Who caught the larger red snapper?

Complete the statement using <, >, or =.

10. 0.13 ____ $\frac{1}{8}$ **11.** $-1\frac{2}{9}$ ____ $-\frac{5}{4}$ **12.** −5.175 ____ $-5\frac{1}{6}$

13. Find one terminating and one repeating decimal between $-1\frac{1}{2}$ and $-1\frac{7}{9}$.

14. The table gives the tidal changes in the water level of a lagoon for every six hours of a given day.

Time	4:00 A.M.	10:00 A.M.	4:00 P.M.	10:00 P.M.
Change (feet)	2.25	$-2\frac{6}{7}$	$-\frac{3}{2}$	$2\frac{1}{3}$

  a. Order the numbers from least to greatest.

  b. At what time(s) did the water level decrease?

  c. What was the largest change in water level?

  d. Did the tidal change in part (c) involve an increase or a decrease in water level?

  e. Will the next tidal change be an increase or decrease in water level? Explain.

15. Let a and b be integers.

  a. When can $\frac{a}{b}$ be written as a negative, repeating decimal between 0 and −1?

  b. When can $\frac{a}{b}$ be written as a negative, terminating decimal between 0 and −1?

  c. When can $\frac{a}{b}$ be written as a negative decimal between 0 and −1 that does not repeat and does not terminate?

2.4 Multiplying Rational Numbers
For use with Exploration 2.4

Learning Target: Find products of rational numbers.

Success Criteria:
- I can explain the rules for multiplying rational numbers.
- I can find products of rational numbers with the same sign.
- I can find products of rational numbers with different signs.

1 EXPLORATION: Finding Products of Rational Numbers

Work with a partner.

a. Write a multiplication expression represented by each area model. Then find the product.

2.4 **Multiplying Rational Numbers** (continued)

b. Complete the table.

	Expression	Product	Expression	Product
i.	0.2×0.9		-0.2×0.9	
ii.	$0.3(0.5)$		$0.3(-0.5)$	
iii.	$\dfrac{1}{4} \cdot \dfrac{1}{2}$		$\dfrac{1}{4} \cdot \left(-\dfrac{1}{2}\right)$	
iv.	$1.2(0.4)$		$-1.2(-0.4)$	
v.	$\dfrac{3}{10}\left(\dfrac{2}{5}\right)$		$-\dfrac{3}{10}\left(-\dfrac{2}{5}\right)$	
vi.	0.6×1.8		-0.6×1.8	
vii.	$1\dfrac{1}{4} \cdot 2\dfrac{1}{2}$		$-1\dfrac{1}{4} \cdot \left(-2\dfrac{1}{2}\right)$	

c. Do the rules for multiplying integers apply to all rational numbers? Explain your reasoning.

Name_____ Date_____

2.4 Notetaking with Vocabulary

Vocabulary:

Notes:

2.4 Self-Assessment

Use the scale below to rate your understanding of the learning target and the success criteria.

1	2	3	4
I do not understand.	I can do it with help.	I can do it on my own.	I can teach someone else.

	Rating	Date
2.4 Multiplying Rational Numbers		
Learning Target: Find products of rational numbers.	1 2 3 4	
I can explain the rules for multiplying rational numbers.	1 2 3 4	
I can find products of rational numbers with the same sign.	1 2 3 4	
I can find products of rational numbers with different signs.	1 2 3 4	

Name _____ Date _____

2.4 Practice

Find the product. Write fractions in simplest form.

1. $1\frac{2}{3}\left(-2\frac{9}{10}\right)$

2. $-\left(3\frac{2}{5}\right)^2$

3. $-1.27 \cdot (-2.02)$

4. Mixed nuts cost $7.80 per pound. You purchase $2\frac{1}{4}$ pounds. What is the total cost of your purchase?

5. Write two fractions whose product is $-\frac{4}{9}$.

Evaluate the expression. Write fractions in simplest form.

6. $-0.2^3 - 4.15(-0.06)$

7. $2\frac{1}{3} \times \left(-4\frac{5}{7}\right) - \left(-\frac{3}{5}\right)^2$

8. A gallon of gasoline costs $2.96. Your car has a 25-gallon gas tank.

    a. Find the cost of filling your gas tank if it is already $\frac{3}{8}$ full.

    b. Your car averages $17\frac{3}{5}$ miles per gallon. After introducing an additive to your gasoline, your car averages $19\frac{1}{5}$ miles per gallon. The company advertised that the additive would give a 10% increase in miles per gallon. Did your car have a 10% increase in miles per gallon? Justify your answer.

9. Use positive or negative integers to fill in the blanks so that the product is $-\frac{1}{6}$. Justify your answer.

$$\frac{\square}{\square} \times \frac{-2}{\square} \times \left(-\frac{\square}{3}\right)$$

10. A school record for the 5K run is 20.15 minutes. Predict the school record after 12 years when the school record decreases by about 0.155 second per year.

11. Use positive or negative integers to fill in the blanks so that the product is -46.25.

$$1\square.5 \times (-3.7\square)$$

Name_____ Date_____

Learning Target: Find quotients of rational numbers.

Success Criteria:
- I can explain the rules for dividing rational numbers.
- I can find quotients of rational numbers with the same sign.
- I can find quotients of rational numbers with different signs.

1 EXPLORATION: Finding Quotients of Rational Numbers

Work with a partner.

a. Write two division expressions represented by the area model. Then find the quotients.

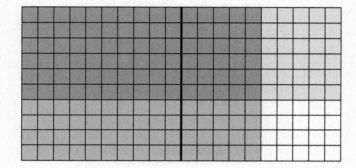

2.5 **Dividing Rational Numbers** (continued)

b. Complete the table.

	Expression	Quotient	Expression	Quotient
i.	$0.9 \div 1.5$		$-0.9 \div 1.5$	
ii.	$1 \div \dfrac{1}{2}$		$-1 \div \dfrac{1}{2}$	
iii.	$2 \div 0.25$		$2 \div (-0.25)$	
iv.	$0 \div \dfrac{4}{5}$		$0 \div \left(-\dfrac{4}{5}\right)$	
v.	$1\dfrac{1}{2} \div 3$		$-1\dfrac{1}{2} \div (-3)$	
vi.	$0.8 \div 0.1$		$-0.8 \div (-0.1)$	

c. Do the rules for dividing integers apply to all rational numbers? Explain your reasoning.

d. Write a real-life story involving the quotient $-0.75 \div 3$. Interpret the quotient in the context of the story.

2.5 Notetaking with Vocabulary

Vocabulary:

Notes:

2.5 Self-Assessment

Use the scale below to rate your understanding of the learning target and the success criteria.

1	2	3	4
I do not understand.	I can do it with help.	I can do it on my own.	I can teach someone else.

	Rating	Date
2.5 Dividing Rational Numbers		
Learning Target: Find quotients of rational numbers.	1 2 3 4	
I can explain the rules for dividing rational numbers.	1 2 3 4	
I can find quotients of rational numbers with the same sign.	1 2 3 4	
I can find quotients of rational numbers with different signs.	1 2 3 4	

Name _____ Date _____

2.5 Practice

Find the quotient. Write fractions in simplest form.

1. $1\frac{5}{6} \div (-30)$

2. $-2\frac{4}{5} \div 10\frac{2}{3}$

3. $14.616 \div (-2.32)$

4. How many three-quarter pound burgers can be made with twelve pounds of hamburger?

5. The table shows the changes in your times (in seconds) at the new skateboard ramp.

Trial	1	2	3	4	5
Change	2.2	−1.4	0.6	−2.3	−1.7

   a. What is your mean change?

   b. After the 6th trial, your mean change was −0.35. What was the change in your time on the 6th trial?

   c. Was your 6th trial faster or slower than your 5th trial? Explain.

Evaluate the expression. Write fractions in simplest form.

6. $5 - 3\frac{9}{10} \div 2\frac{3}{5}$

7. $-3.4^2 \div 1.7 + 7.5$

8. $\dfrac{5\frac{2}{3}}{2\frac{1}{6}}$

9. $\dfrac{-\frac{3}{10}}{1-\frac{2}{5}}$

10. $\dfrac{\frac{15}{8}}{\frac{5}{2}-\frac{1}{4}}$

11. $\dfrac{2\frac{2}{3}+1\frac{5}{6}}{\left(\frac{4}{5}\right)\left(-\frac{9}{2}\right)}$

12. A gallon of gasoline costs \$2.96. Your car can travel 28.8 miles on each gallon of gasoline.

   a. You take a trip of length $705\frac{3}{5}$ miles. How much money do you spend on gasoline?

   b. You take the same trip the next year, with the same car. You spend \$90.65 on gasoline. What is the percent increase in the price per gallon of gasoline?

Name_____ Date_____

Chapter 2 Chapter Self-Assessment

Use the scale below to rate your understanding of the learning target and the success criteria.

1 I do not understand.

2 I can do it with help.

3 I can do it on my own.

4 I can teach someone else.

	Rating	Date
2.1 Multiplying Integers		
Learning Target: Find products of integers.	1 2 3 4	
I can explain the rules for multiplying integers.	1 2 3 4	
I can find products of integers with the same sign.	1 2 3 4	
I can find products of integers with different signs.	1 2 3 4	
2.2 Dividing Integers		
Learning Target: Find quotients of integers.	1 2 3 4	
I can explain the rules for dividing integers.	1 2 3 4	
I can find quotients of integers with the same sign.	1 2 3 4	
I can find quotients of integers with different signs.	1 2 3 4	
2.3 Converting Between Fractions and Decimals		
Learning Target: Convert between different forms of rational numbers.	1 2 3 4	
I can explain the difference between terminating and repeating decimals.	1 2 3 4	
I can write fractions and mixed numbers as decimals.	1 2 3 4	
I can write decimals as fractions and mixed numbers.	1 2 3 4	

Chapter 2 Chapter Self-Assessment (continued)

	Rating	Date
2.4 Multiplying Rational Numbers		
Learning Target: Find products of rational numbers.	1 2 3 4	
I can explain the rules for multiplying rational numbers.	1 2 3 4	
I can find products of rational numbers with the same sign.	1 2 3 4	
I can find products of rational numbers with different signs.	1 2 3 4	
2.5 Dividing Rational Numbers		
Learning Target: Find quotients of rational numbers.	1 2 3 4	
I can explain the rules for dividing rational numbers.	1 2 3 4	
I can find quotients of rational numbers with the same sign.	1 2 3 4	
I can find quotients of rational numbers with different signs.	1 2 3 4	

Name_____ Date_____

Evaluate the expression when $x = \frac{1}{2}$ and $y = -3$.

1. $-4xy$

2. $6x - 3y$

3. $-5y + 8x + 1$

4. $-x^2 - y + 2$

5. $2x + 4\left(x + \frac{1}{2}\right) + 7$

6. $2(4x - 1)^2 - 3$

7. Find the area of the garden when $x = 2$ feet.

3x ft

2x ft

Chapter 3 Review & Refresh (continued)

Find the product or quotient. Write fractions in simplest form.

8. $-\frac{3}{10} \times \frac{5}{9}$

9. $-\frac{4}{11} \times \left(-4\frac{1}{8}\right)$

10. $1\frac{1}{5} \div -\frac{2}{15}$

11. $-2\frac{2}{9} \div 2\frac{1}{12}$

Find the sum or difference. Write fractions in simplest form.

12. $\frac{6}{25} - \left(-\frac{1}{5}\right)$

13. $-5\frac{7}{8} - \left(-2\frac{1}{3}\right)$

14. $9.7 - 12.4$

15. $-1.9 + 13.8$

Name_____ Date_____

 3.1 **Algebraic Expressions**
For use with Exploration 3.1

Learning Target: Simplify algebraic expressions.

Success Criteria:
- I can identify terms and like terms of algebraic expressions.
- I can combine like terms to simplify algebraic expressions.
- I can write and simplify algebraic expressions to solve real-life problems.

1 **EXPLORATION: Simplifying Algebraic Expressions**

Work with a partner.

a. Choose a value of x other than 0 or 1 for the last column in the table. Complete the table by evaluating each algebraic expression for each value of x. What do you notice?

	Expression	Value When		
		$x = 0$	$x = 1$	$x = ?$
A.	$-\frac{1}{3} + x + \frac{7}{3}$			
B.	$0.5x + 3 - 1.5x - 1$			
C.	$2x + 6$			
D.	$x + 4$			
E.	$-2x + 2$			
F.	$\frac{1}{2}x - x + \frac{3}{2}x + 4$			
G.	$-4.8x + 2 - x + 3.8x$			
H.	$x + 2$			
I.	$-x + 2$			
J.	$3x + 2 - x + 4$			

3.1 Algebraic Expressions (continued)

b. How can you use properties of operations to justify your answers in part (a)? Explain your reasoning.

c. To subtract a number, you can add its opposite. Does a similar rule apply to the terms of an algebraic expression? Explain your reasoning.

Name_____ Date _____

Vocabulary:

Notes:

3.1 **Self-Assessment**

Use the scale below to rate your understanding of the learning target and the success criteria.

1	**2**	**3**	**4**
I do not understand.	I can do it with help.	I can do it on my own.	I can teach someone else.

	Rating	Date
3.1 Algebraic Expressions		
Learning Target: Simplify algebraic expressions.	1 2 3 4	
I can identify terms and like terms of algebraic expressions.	1 2 3 4	
I can combine like terms to simplify algebraic expressions.	1 2 3 4	
I can write and simplify algebraic expressions to solve real-life problems.	1 2 3 4	

Big Ideas Math: Modeling Real Life Grade 7
Student Journal
53

Name _____ Date _____

3.1 Practice

Identify the terms and like terms in the expression.

1. $1.3x - 2.7x^2 - 5.4x + 3$

2. $10 - \frac{3}{10}m + 6m^2 + \frac{2}{5}m$

Simplify the expression.

3. $-\frac{15}{4}b + \frac{5}{6}b$

4. $9y - 15y + 12 - 6y$

5. Write an expression in simplest form that represents the perimeter of the polygon.

6. Danielle is x years old. Her sister is 5 years older and her brother is half Danielle's age. Write an expression in simplest form for the sum of their ages.

7. You buy x packs of pencils, twice as many packs of erasers, and three times as many rolls of tape. Write an expression in simplest form for the total amount of money you spent.

8. Evaluate the expression $-\frac{2}{3}x - 4 + \frac{1}{2}x - 3 + \frac{5}{6}x$ when $x = 3$ before and after simplifying. Which method do you prefer, *before simplifying* or *after simplifying*? Explain.

9. Write an expression with seven different terms that is equivalent to $9x - 4x^2 - 15 + y$. Justify your answer.

10. For what value(s) of x is the expression $3x - \frac{1}{4} + 5$ equivalent to the expression $-\frac{1}{4} + 5$? Explain.

Name_____ Date _____

3.2 Adding and Subtracting Linear Expressions
For use with Exploration 3.2

Learning Target: Find sums and differences of linear expressions.

Success Criteria:
- I can explain the difference between linear and nonlinear expressions.
- I can find opposites of terms that include variables.
- I can apply properties of operations to add and subtract linear expressions.

---

1 EXPLORATION: Using Algebra Tiles

Work with a partner. You can use algebra tiles shown at the right to find sums and differences of algebraic expressions.

a. How can you use algebra tiles to model a sum of terms that equals 0? Explain your reasoning.

b. Write each sum or difference modeled below. Then use the algebra tiles to simplify the expression.

$$\left(\boxed{+} \; \boxed{+} \boxed{+} \boxed{+} \boxed{+} \right) + \left(\boxed{\begin{smallmatrix} + \\ + \end{smallmatrix}} \; \boxed{-} \boxed{-} \boxed{-} \right)$$

$$\left(\boxed{\begin{smallmatrix} + \\ + \end{smallmatrix}} \; \boxed{\begin{smallmatrix} - - - - \\ - - - \end{smallmatrix}} \right) + \left(\boxed{\begin{smallmatrix} - \\ - \\ - \end{smallmatrix}} \; \boxed{\begin{smallmatrix} + + + \\ + + \end{smallmatrix}} \right)$$

$$\left(\boxed{+} \; \boxed{-} \boxed{-} \boxed{-} \right) - \left(\boxed{+} \; \boxed{-} \boxed{-} \boxed{-} \right)$$

3.2   **Adding and Subtracting Linear Expressions** (continued)

$$\left(\begin{array}{c} \boxed{-} \\ \boxed{-} \end{array} \boxed{+}\,\boxed{+}\,\boxed{+}\,\boxed{+}\,\boxed{+} \right) - \left(\boxed{+}\,\boxed{-} \right)$$

c. Write two algebraic expressions of the form $ax + b$, where a and b are rational numbers. Find the sum and difference of the expressions.

2   EXPLORATION: Using Properties of Operations

Work with a partner.

a. Do algebraic expressions, such as $2x$, $-3y$, and $3z + 1$, have additive inverses? How do you know?

b. How can you find the sums and differences modeled in Exploration 1 without using algebra tiles? Explain your reasoning.

Name_____ Date_____

3.2 Notetaking with Vocabulary

Vocabulary:

Notes:

3.2 Self-Assessment

Use the scale below to rate your understanding of the learning target and the success criteria.

1	2	3	4
I do not understand.	I can do it with help.	I can do it on my own.	I can teach someone else.

	Rating	Date
3.2 Adding and Subtracting Linear Expressions		
Learning Target: Find sums and differences of linear expressions.	1 2 3 4	
I can explain the difference between linear and nonlinear expressions.	1 2 3 4	
I can find opposites of terms that include variables.	1 2 3 4	
I can apply properties of operations to add and subtract linear expressions.	1 2 3 4	

3.2 Practice

Find the sum.

1. $(-1.2t + 5) + (3t + 2)$

2. $\left(\frac{7}{4}k + 9\right) + \left(\frac{1}{3}k - 3\right)$

3. $(-0.3s - 2) + (5 - 3.4s) + (5r + 2)$

4. $\left(\frac{1}{6}p - 3\right) + (3q - 1.7) + \left(-\frac{1}{3}p + 4\right)$

5. You are collecting pairs of socks and toothbrushes for a local charity. After d days, you have collected $(4d + 5)$ pairs of socks and $(3d + 7)$ toothbrushes.

   a. Write an expression that represents the total number of items that have been collected.

   b. How many more pairs of socks than toothbrushes have been collected on day 7?

Find the difference.

6. $(8.2k - 6) - (4.5 - 9k)$

7. $\left(-\frac{3}{5} + 2g\right) - \left(4 + \frac{2}{3}g\right)$

8. $\left(\frac{2}{7}x - 3\right) - \left(\frac{5}{2} + \frac{1}{5}y\right)$

9. $(3 - 2.1z) - (1.7w + 9) - (-8 - 3z)$

10. The expression $7n - 19$ represents the perimeter of the triangle.

    a. What is the length of the third side?

    b. What are the lengths of the three sides of the triangle when $n = 5$? Is the triangle a right triangle? Explain.

    c. What are the lengths of the three sides of the triangle when $n = 7$? Is the triangle a right triangle? Explain.

11. Consider $ax + b$ and $cx + d$, two linear expressions.

    a. Find values for a, b, c, and d, such that the expression $(ax + b) - (cx + d)$ is a linear expression.

    b. Find values for a, b, c, and d, such that the expression $(ax + b) - (cx + d)$ is not a linear expression.

3.3 The Distributive Property
For use with Exploration 3.3

Learning Target: Apply the Distributive Property to generate equivalent expressions.

Success Criteria: • I can explain how to apply the Distributive Property.
  • I can use the Distributive Property to simplify algebraic expressions.

1 EXPLORATION: Using Models to Write Expressions

Work with a partner.

a. Write an expression that represents the area of the shaded region in each figure.

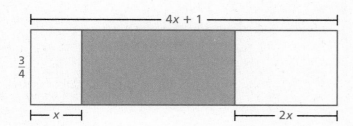

3.3 The Distributive Property (continued)

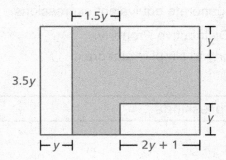

b. Compare your expressions in part (a) with other groups in your class.
Did other groups write expressions that look different than yours?
If so, determine whether the expressions are equivalent.

3.3 Notetaking with Vocabulary

Vocabulary:

Notes:

3.3 Self-Assessment

Use the scale below to rate your understanding of the learning target and the success criteria.

1	2	3	4
I do not understand.	I can do it with help.	I can do it on my own.	I can teach someone else.

	Rating	Date
3.3 The Distributive Property		
Learning Target: Apply the Distributive Property to generate equivalent expressions.	1 2 3 4	
I can explain how to apply the Distributive Property.	1 2 3 4	
I can use the Distributive Property to simplify algebraic expressions.	1 2 3 4	

Name _____ Date _____

3.3 Practice

Simplify the expression.

1. $60m - 15(4 - 8m) + 20$

2. $4(5.8 - 9x) + 8.2 + 22x$

3. $\frac{5}{3}(5x + 9) + \frac{4}{5}(1 - 9x)$

4. $4(2.5g - 4) + 3(1.2g - 2)$

5. $\frac{1}{5}(-15w - 20) + \frac{1}{2}(3 - 4w)$

6. $\frac{1}{8}(16k - 24) + \frac{1}{5}(2 + 10k)$

7. $(12 + 7.2b) - 3(0.9b - 4)$

8. $\frac{1}{4}(16j - 12) - \frac{1}{9}(18j + 45)$

9. You are selling tickets to a play. You have sold $(3t + 2)$ tickets for $5 each and $(2t + 5)$ tickets for $7 each.

   a. Write an expression that represents the total number of tickets sold so far. Then simplify the expression.

   b. Write an expression that represents the total amount of money received for the tickets that have been sold. Then simplify the expression.

   c. When $t = 3$, what is the total amount of money received?

Draw a diagram that shows how the expression can represent the area of a figure. Then simplify the expression.

10. $8(3x - 1)$

11. $(5 + 2)(x + 3x)$

12. The length of a rectangular field is 30 more than twice its width. Write an expression in simplest form for the perimeter of the field in terms of its width w.

13. Which of the following is not equivalent? Explain.

   a. $5(2x - 7)$
   b. $(2x - 7)(5)$
   c. $5(7 - 2x)$
   d. $5(-7 + 2x)$

14. Your friend asks you to perform the following steps.

   1) Pick any number except 0.

   2) Subtract 5 from your number.

   3) Multiply the result by 2.

   4) Add 10 to the result.

   5) Divide the result by 4.

   Your friend says, "Your original number was ____!" Explain how your friend knew your original number.

3.4 Factoring Expressions
For use with Exploration 3.4

Learning Target: Factor algebraic expressions.

Success Criteria:
- I can identify the greatest common factor of terms, including variable terms.
- I can use the Distributive Property to factor algebraic expressions.
- I can write a term as a product involving a given factor.

---

1 EXPLORATION: Finding Dimensions

Work with a partner.

a. The models show the areas (in square units) of parts of rectangles. Use the models to find the missing values that complete the expressions. Explain your reasoning.

$$\frac{4}{5} + \frac{8}{5} = ?\,(\,?\,+\,?\,)$$

$$\frac{3}{2}x + \frac{1}{2} = ?\,(\,?\,+\,?\,)$$

3.4 **Factoring Expressions** (continued)

$$2.5x + 3.75y = ?\,(? + ?)$$

b. Are the expressions you wrote in part (a) equivalent to the original expressions? Explain your reasoning.

c. Explain how you can use the Distributive Property to find rational number factors of an expression.

3.4 Notetaking with Vocabulary

Vocabulary:

Notes:

3.4 Self-Assessment

Use the scale below to rate your understanding of the learning target and the success criteria.

1	2	3	4
I do not understand.	I can do it with help.	I can do it on my own.	I can teach someone else.

	Rating	Date
3.4 Factoring Expressions		
Learning Target: Factor algebraic expressions.	1 2 3 4	
I can identify the greatest common factor of terms, including variable terms.	1 2 3 4	
I can use the Distributive Property to factor algebraic expressions.	1 2 3 4	
I can write a term as a product involving a given factor.	1 2 3 4	

3.4 Practice

Factor the expression using the GCF.

1. $21s + 15$

2. $32v + 24w$

3. $12y - 42z$

Factor out the coefficient of the variable term.

4. $1.2k + 2.4$

5. $3f + 5$

6. $\frac{3}{10}x - \frac{3}{5}$

7. Factor $-\frac{1}{3}$ out of $-\frac{1}{3}x - 12$.

8. Factor $-\frac{1}{6}$ out of $-\frac{1}{3}x + \frac{5}{6}y$.

9. The area of the rectangle is $(18x - 12)$ square inches. Write an expression that represents the length of the rectangle (in inches).

6 in.

10. A concession stand sells hamburgers. The revenue from the hamburgers is $(30x + 45)$ dollars.

  a. The price of a hamburger is $5. Write an expression that represents the number of hamburgers sold.

  b. The revenue from drinks is $(63x + 84)$ dollars. The price of a drink is $3. Write an expression that represents the number of drinks sold.

  c. Write and simplify an expression that represents how many more drinks than hamburgers were sold.

11. The formula for the area of a triangle is $A = \frac{1}{2}bh$. A triangle has an area of $\left(\frac{1}{12}x + \frac{7}{30}\right)$.

  a. Write a multiplication expression that can represent the product of $\frac{1}{2}$ and the base and the height of the triangle.

  b. Write a multiplication expression that can represent the product of $\frac{1}{2}$ and the base and the height of the triangle, where the factor containing the x-term does not have fractions.

Name_____ Date _____

Chapter Self-Assessment

Use the scale below to rate your understanding of the learning target and the success criteria.

1	2	3	4
I do not understand.	I can do it with help.	I can do it on my own.	I can teach someone else.

	Rating	Date
3.1 Algebraic Expressions		
Learning Target: Simplify algebraic expressions.	1 2 3 4	
I can identify terms and like terms of algebraic expressions.	1 2 3 4	
I can combine like terms to simplify algebraic expressions.	1 2 3 4	
I can write and simplify algebraic expressions to solve real-life problems.	1 2 3 4	
3.2 Adding and Subtraction Linear Expressions		
Learning Target: Find sums and differences of linear expressions.	1 2 3 4	
I can explain the difference between linear and nonlinear expressions.	1 2 3 4	
I can find opposites of terms that include variables.	1 2 3 4	
I can apply properties of operations to add and subtract linear expressions.	1 2 3 4	
3.3 The Distributive Property		
Learning Target: Apply the Distributive Property to generate equivalent expressions.	1 2 3 4	
I can explain how to apply the Distributive Property.	1 2 3 4	
I can use the Distributive Property to simplify algebraic expressions.	1 2 3 4	

Chapter 3   Chapter Self-Assessment (continued)

	Rating	Date
3.4 Factoring Expressions		
Learning Target: Factor algebraic expressions.	1 2 3 4	
I can identify the greatest common factor of terms, including variable terms.	1 2 3 4	
I can use the Distributive Property to factor algebraic expressions.	1 2 3 4	
I can write a term as a product involving a given factor.	1 2 3 4	

Name_____ Date _____

Review & Refresh

Write the phrase as an algebraic expression.

1. the sum of eight and a number y

2. six less than a number p

3. the product of seven and a number m

4. eight less than the product of eleven and a number c

5. a number r decreased by the quotient of a number r and two

6. the product of nine and the sum of a number z and four

Chapter 4 Review & Refresh (continued)

Complete the number sentence with < or >.

7. $\frac{3}{4}$ ___ 0.2

8. $\frac{7}{8}$ ___ 0.7

9. -0.6 ___ $-\frac{2}{3}$

10. -1.76 ___ 1.75

11. $\frac{17}{3}$ ___ 6

12. 1.8 ___ $\frac{31}{16}$

13. Your height is 5 feet and $1\frac{5}{8}$ inches. Your friend's height is 5.6 feet. Who is taller? Explain.

Name_____ Date_____

4.1 Solving Equations Using Addition or Subtraction
For use with Exploration 4.1

Learning Target: Write and solve equations using addition or subtraction.

Success Criteria:
- I can apply the Addition and Subtraction Properties of Equality to produce equivalent equations.
- I can solve equations using addition or subtraction.
- I can apply equations involving addition or subtraction to solve real-life problems.

1 EXPLORATION: Using Algebra Tiles to Solve Equations

Work with a partner.

   a. Use the examples to explain the meaning of each property.

        Addition Property of Equality: $x + 2 = 1$

                                        $x + 2 + 5 = 1 + 5$

        Subtraction Property of Equality: $x + 2 = 1$

                                          $x + 2 - 1 = 1 - 1$

Are these properties true for equations involving negative numbers? Explain your reasoning.

4.1 **Solving Equations Using Addition or Subtraction** (continued)

b. Write the four equations modeled by the algebra tiles. Explain how you can use algebra tiles to solve each equation. Then find the solutions.

c. How can you solve each equation in part (b) without using algebra tiles?

4.1 Notetaking with Vocabulary

Vocabulary:

Notes:

4.1 Self-Assessment

Use the scale below to rate your understanding of the learning target and the success criteria.

1	**2**	**3**	**4**
I do not understand.	I can do it with help.	I can do it on my own.	I can teach someone else.

	Rating	Date
4.1 Solving Equations Using Addition or Subtraction		
Learning Target: Write and solve equations using addition or subtraction.	1　2　3　4	
I can apply the Addition and Subtraction Properties of Equality to produce equivalent equations.	1　2　3　4	
I can solve equations using addition or subtraction.	1　2　3　4	
I can apply equations involving addition or subtraction to solve real-life problems.	1　2　3　4	

4.1 Practice

Solve the equation. Check your solution.

1. $-4.5 = m + 1.9$

2. $10\frac{2}{3} = r + 12\frac{1}{6}$

3. $b + 4.006 = 9$

4. $-7\frac{5}{8} = 1\frac{5}{6} + d$

5. $f - \frac{2}{15} = 6\frac{3}{5}$

6. $-10.216 + c = -12.014$

Write the word sentence as an equation. Then solve the equation.

7. 27 is 12 more than a number x.

8. The difference of a number p and –9 is 12.

9. 35 less than a number m is –72.

10. You swim the 50-meter freestyle in 28.12 seconds. This is 0.14 second less than your previous fastest time. Write and solve an equation to find your previous fastest time.

11. The perimeter of a rectangular backyard is $32\frac{1}{2}$ meters. The two shorter sides are each $7\frac{3}{8}$ meters long. Write and solve an equation to find the length of the two longer sides? (*Hint:* The sum of the shorter side and the longer side is equal to half of the perimeter.)

12. The wind chill when the airplane lands in Minneapolis is –70.2°F, which is 140.8°F less than the wind chill when the airplane took off in Orlando. Write and solve an equation to find the wind chill when the airplane took off in Orlando.

13. Your cell phone bill in August was $61.43, which was $21.75 more than your bill in July. Your cell phone bill in July was $13.62 less than your bill in June. What was your cell phone bill in June?

Solve the equation.

14. $|x| - 10.5 = 4.3$

15. $|x + 2| - 7 = 5$

16. Find the value of $3x + 2$ when $x - 5 = -8$.

17. Find the values of $x - 4$ when $|x| + 1 = 3$.

4.2 Solving Equations Using Multiplication or Division
For use with Exploration 4.2

Learning Target: Write and solve equations using multiplication or division.

Success Criteria:
- I can apply the Multiplication and Division Properties of Equality to produce equivalent equations.
- I can solve equations using multiplication or division.
- I can apply equations involving multiplication or division to solve real-life problems.

---

1 EXPLORATION: Using Algebra Tiles to Solve Equations

Work with a partner.

a. Use the examples to explain the meaning of each property.

$$\text{Multiplication Property of Equality:} \qquad 3x = 1$$
$$2 \cdot 3x = 2 \cdot 1$$

$$\text{Division Property of Equality:} \qquad 3x = 1$$
$$\frac{3x}{4} = \frac{1}{4}$$

Are these properties true for equations involving negative numbers? Explain your reasoning.

4.2 **Solving Equations Using Multiplication or Division** (continued)

b. Write the three equations modeled by the algebra tiles. Explain how you can use algebra tiles to solve each equation. Then find the solutions.

c. How can you solve each equation in part (b) without using algebra tiles?

4.2 Notetaking with Vocabulary

Vocabulary:

Notes:

4.2 Self-Assessment

Use the scale below to rate your understanding of the learning target and the success criteria.

1	**2**	**3**	**4**
I do not understand.	I can do it with help.	I can do it on my own.	I can teach someone else.

	Rating	Date
4.2 Solving Equations Using Multiplication or Division		
Learning Target: Write and solve equations using multiplication or division.	1 2 3 4	
I can apply the Multiplication and Division Properties of Equality to produce equivalent equations.	1 2 3 4	
I can solve equations using multiplication or division.	1 2 3 4	
I can apply equations involving multiplication or division to solve real-life problems.	1 2 3 4	

4.2 Practice

Solve the equation. Check your solution.

1. $-14p = -21$

2. $-\dfrac{8}{15}k = -4$

3. $-7.24q = 17.014$

4. $\dfrac{g}{0.003} = -2.8$

5. $-\dfrac{10}{21}c = -\dfrac{15}{28}$

6. $18 = -\dfrac{6}{11}h$

7. You order an entrée for $12.00. You pay $0.78 in taxes. Write and solve an equation to determine the tax rate.

8. If a project is handed in late, you receive $\dfrac{8}{9}$ of your earned points. You received 72 points on your late project. Write and solve an equation to determine how many points you lost.

9. Write a multiplication equation that has a solution of -14.8.

10. Write a division equation that has a solution of $-\dfrac{9}{14}$.

Write the word sentence as an equation. Then solve the equation.

11. A number divided by $\dfrac{1}{2}$ is 10.

12. The product of a number and -12 is -8.

13. The quotient of 9.75 and a number is -6.5

14. There are 92 students in a room. They are separated into 18 groups. How many students are in each group? How many students are not in a group?

15. A bus token costs $1.75.

   a. You spend $15.75 on tokens. Write and solve an equation to find how many tokens you purchase.

   b. If you purchase 10 tokens, you get 2 free tokens. Write and solve an equation to find the approximate reduced price of each token when purchasing this special.

   c. You also receive free tokens if you purchase 20 tokens. The reduced price for each token is $1.40. Write and solve an equation to find how many free tokens you receive when purchasing this special.

16. Solve $\dfrac{1}{3}|z| = 2$.

Name_____ Date_____

4.3 Solving Two-Step Equations
For use with Exploration 4.3

Learning Target: Write and solve two-step equations.

Success Criteria:
- I can apply properties of equality to produce equivalent equations.
- I can solve two-step equations using the basic operations.
- I can apply two-step equations to solve real-life problems.

1 EXPLORATION: Using Algebra Tiles to Solve Equations

Work with a partner.

a. What is being modeled by the algebra tiles below? What is the solution?

b. Use properties of equality to solve the original equation in part (a). How do your steps compare to the steps performed with algebra tiles?

4.3 **Solving Two-Step Equations** (continued)

c. Write the three equations modeled by the algebra tiles below. Then solve each equation using algebra tiles. Check your answers using properties of equality.

d. Explain how to solve an equation of the form $ax + b = c$ for x.

4.3 Notetaking with Vocabulary

Vocabulary:

Notes:

4.3 Self-Assessment

Use the scale below to rate your understanding of the learning target and the success criteria.

1	2	3	4
I do not understand.	I can do it with help.	I can do it on my own.	I can teach someone else.

	Rating	Date
4.3 Solving Two-Step Equations		
Learning Target: Write and solve two-step equations.	1 2 3 4	
I can apply properties of equality to produce equivalent equations.	1 2 3 4	
I can solve two-step equations using the basic operations.	1 2 3 4	
I can apply two-step equations to solve real-life problems.	1 2 3 4	

4.3 Practice

Solve the equation. Check your solution.

1. $25 = 4.5z + 12$

2. $5.25s - 2.01 = -8.94$

3. $16 + 2.4c = 22.5$

4. $4h + \frac{1}{3} = \frac{3}{4}$

5. $\frac{1}{7}f - 5\frac{1}{2} = \frac{9}{14}$

6. $-\frac{1}{2}u + \frac{3}{5} = \frac{1}{6}$

7. You purchased $132.49 worth of wheels and bearings for your skateboards. The shop charges $15 per board to install them. The total cost is $192.49. Write and solve an equation to determine how many skateboards will be repaired.

8. A music download service charges a flat fee each month and $0.99 per download. The total cost for downloading 27 songs this month is $42.72. Write and solve an equation to determine the flat fee.

Solve the equation. Check your solution.

9. $-5(m + 4) = 27$

10. $-12(a - 2) = -50$

11. $-5x - 2x + 3x = 9$

12. The perimeter of a triangle is 60 feet. One leg is 12 feet long. Of the two unknown sides, one the them is twice as long as the other. Find the lengths of the two unknown sides.

13. Sally picks seashells by the seashore. She lost 17 of them on her way home. With the remaining seashells, she planned to fill 5 jars with the same number of seashells in each. How many seashells did Sally originally pick?

    a. You do not have enough information to solve this problem. The number of seashells in each jar is the same as the number portion of her street address, which is a 2-digit number. The first digit is 5. The last digit is 9 less than 3 times the first digit. How many seashells did Sally plan to put in each jar?

    b. By working backwards, determine how many seashells Sally originally picked.

    c. The 5 jars that Sally chose would not each hold that many seashells. In her search for a 6th jar, she discovered a few seashells in her pocket. What are possible values for the number of seashells in each of the 6 jars and the number of seashells discovered in her pocket, such that there are no seashells left over?

Name_____ Date _____

Learning Target: Write inequalities and represent solutions of inequalities on number lines.

Success Criteria:
- I can write word sentences as inequalities.
- I can determine whether a value is a solution of an inequality.
- I can graph the solutions of inequalities.

1 EXPLORATION: Understanding Inequality Statements

Work with a partner. Create a number line on the floor with both positive and negative numbers.

a. For each statement, stand at a number on your number line that could represent the situation. On what other numbers can you stand?

At least 3 students from our school are in a chess tournament.

Your ring size is less than 7.5.

The temperature is no more than −1 degree Fahrenheit.

4.4 **Writing and Graphing Inequalities (continued)**

The elevation of a frogfish is greater than $-8\frac{1}{2}$ meters.

b. How can you represent all of the solutions for each statement in part (a) on a number line?

4.4 Notetaking with Vocabulary

Vocabulary:

Notes:

4.4 Self-Assessment

Use the scale below to rate your understanding of the learning target and the success criteria.

1	*2*	*3*	*4*
I do not understand.	I can do it with help.	I can do it on my own.	I can teach someone else.

	Rating	Date
4.4 Writing and Graphing Inequalities		
Learning Target: Write inequalities and represent solutions of inequalities on number lines.	1 2 3 4	
I can write word sentences as inequalities.	1 2 3 4	
I can determine whether a value is a solution of an inequality.	1 2 3 4	
I can graph the solutions of inequalities.	1 2 3 4	

4.4 Practice

Write an inequality for the graph. Then, in words, describe all the values of x that make the inequality true.

1.

2.

Write the word sentence as an inequality.

3. A number x is at least 15.

4. A number r added to 3.7 is less than 1.2.

5. A number h divided by 2 is more than –5.

6. A number a minus 8.2 is no greater than 12.

Tell whether the given value is a solution of the inequality.

7. $p + 1.7 \geq -4;\ p = -9$

8. $\frac{3}{4} - d > \frac{1}{3};\ d = \frac{1}{2}$

9. $5t < 4 - t;\ t = -3$

10. $\frac{q}{5} < q - 20;\ q = 15$

Graph the inequality on a number line.

11. $\ell \leq 3.5$

12. $m > -15$

13. To get a job at the local restaurant, you must be at least 16 years old. Write an inequality that represents this situation.

14. In order to qualify for a college scholarship, you must have acceptable scores in either the SAT or the ACT along with the following requirements: a minimum GPA of 3.5; at least 12 credits of college preparatory academic courses; and at least 75 hours of community service.

   a. Write and graph three inequalities that represent the requirements.

   b. Your cousin has a GPA of 3.6, 15 credits of college preparatory class, and 65 hours of community service. Other than the test scores, does your cousin satisfy the requirements? Explain.

15. Which of the following is not equivalent? Explain.

   A number x is at most 3.

   A number x is not greater than 3.

   A number x is less than 3.

   A number x is less than or equal to 3.

Name_____ Date_____

4.5 Solving Inequalities Using Addition or Subtraction
For use with Exploration 4.5

Learning Target: Write and solve inequalities using addition or subtraction.

Success Criteria:
- I can apply the Addition and Subtraction Properties of Inequality to produce equivalent inequalities.
- I can solve inequalities using addition or subtraction.
- I can apply inequalities involving addition or subtraction to solve real-life problems.

1 EXPLORATION: Writing Inequalities

Work with a partner. Use two number cubes on which the odd numbers are negative on one of the number cubes and the even numbers are negative on the other number cube.

Roll the number cubes. Write an inequality that compares the numbers.

Roll one of the number cubes. Add the number to each side of the inequality and record your result.

Repeat the previous two steps five more times.

4.5 **Solving Inequalities Using Addition or Subtraction** (continued)

a. When you add the same number to each side of an inequality, does the inequality remain true? Explain your reasoning.

b. When you subtract the same number from each side of an inequality, does the inequality remain true? Use inequalities generated by number cubes to justify your answer.

c. Use your results in parts (a) and (b) to make a conjecture about how to solve an inequality of the form $x + a < b$ for x.

Name_____ Date _____

4.5 Notetaking with Vocabulary

Vocabulary:

Notes:

4.5 Self-Assessment

Use the scale below to rate your understanding of the learning target and the success criteria.

1	2	3	4
I do not understand.	I can do it with help.	I can do it on my own.	I can teach someone else.

	Rating	Date
4.5 Solving Inequalities Using Addition or Subtraction		
Learning Target: Write and solve inequalities using addition or subtraction.	1 2 3 4	
I can apply the Addition and Subtraction Properties of Inequality to produce equivalent inequalities.	1 2 3 4	
I can solve inequalities using addition or subtraction.	1 2 3 4	
I can apply inequalities involving addition or subtraction to solve real-life problems.	1 2 3 4	

Name _____ Date _____

4.5 Practice

Solve the inequality. Graph the solution.

1. $w - 1.8 < 2.5$

2. $v + \frac{1}{3} > 8$

3. $\frac{2}{5} < \frac{4}{5} + k$

4. $q + \frac{3}{4} \geq -\frac{1}{4}$

5. $7.4 > c + 3.9$

6. $p - 10.2 > 3.5$

7. You and two friends are diving for lobster. The maximum number of lobsters you may have on your boat is 18. You currently have 7 lobsters.

   a. Write and solve an inequality that represents the additional lobsters that you may catch.

   b. Another friend comes on your boat and he has 3 lobsters. You may now have 24 lobsters on your boat. Write and solve an inequality that represents the additional lobsters that you may catch.

   c. How many lobsters is each person allowed to catch?

Write and solve an inequality that represents x.

8. The length is greater than the width.

9. The perimeter is less than or equal to 50 inches.

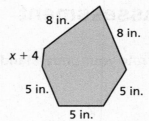

10. The solution of $w - c > -3.4$ is $w > -1.4$. What is the value of c?

11. Describe all numbers that are solutions to $|x| < 5$.

12. The *triangle inequality theorem* states that the sum of the lengths of any two sides of a triangle is greater than the length of the third side. A triangle has side lengths of 6 inches and 17 inches. What are the possible values for the length of the third side? Explain how you found your answer.

13. The possible values of x are given by $x - 5 \geq 7$. What is the least possible value of $9x$? Explain your reasoning.

4.6 Solving Inequalities Using Multiplication or Division
For use with Exploration 4.6

Learning Target: Write and solve inequalities using multiplication or division.

Success Criteria:
- I can apply the Multiplication and Division Properties of Inequality to produce equivalent inequalities.
- I can solve inequalities using multiplication or division.
- I can apply inequalities involving multiplication or division to solve real-life problems.

1 EXPLORATION: Writing Inequalities

Work with a partner. Use two number cubes on which the odd numbers are negative on one of the number cubes and the even numbers are negative on the other number cube.

Roll the number cubes. Write an inequality that compares the numbers.

Roll one of the number cubes. Multiply each side of the inequality by the number and record your result.

Repeat the previous two steps nine more times.

4.6 **Solving Inequalities Using Multiplication or Division** (continued)

a. When you multiply each side of an inequality by the same number, does the inequality remain true? Explain your reasoning?

b. When you divide each side of an inequality by the same number, does the inequality remain true? Use inequalities generated by number cubes to justify your answer.

c. Use your results in parts (a) and (b) to make a conjecture about how to solve an inequality of the form $ax < b$ for x when $a > 0$ and when $a < 0$.

4.6 Notetaking with Vocabulary

Vocabulary:

Notes:

4.6 Self-Assessment

Use the scale below to rate your understanding of the learning target and the success criteria.

1	**2**	**3**	**4**
I do not understand.	I can do it with help.	I can do it on my own.	I can teach someone else.

	Rating	Date
4.6 Solving Inequalities Using Multiplication or Division		
Learning Target: Write and solve inequalities using multiplication or division.	1 2 3 4	
I can apply the Multiplication and Division Properties of Inequality to produce equivalent inequalities.	1 2 3 4	
I can solve inequalities using multiplication or division.	1 2 3 4	
I can apply inequalities involving multiplication or division to solve real-life problems.	1 2 3 4	

4.6 Practice

Solve the inequality. Graph the solution.

1. $3y \le \dfrac{3}{4}$

2. $\dfrac{s}{3.1} \ge 4.5$

3. $-\dfrac{4}{5} < 2x$

4. $-\dfrac{d}{2} > \dfrac{3}{8}$

5. $-1.2 \le -0.8r$

6. $\dfrac{j}{-5.2} \le -1.5$

Write the word sentence as an inequality. Then solve the inequality.

7. A number divided by 5 is at least 4.

8. The product of 2 and a number is at most –6.

9. The solution of $cx \ge -4$ is $x \ge -8$. What is the value of c?

10. The height of a room is 10 feet. You are building shelving from the floor to the ceiling.

   a. Each shelf requires 8 inches. Write and solve an inequality that represents the number of shelves that can be made.

   b. You forgot to include the thickness of each shelf in your measurements. The amount of space needed for each shelf is actually 10 inches. Write and solve an inequality that represents the number of shelves that can be made.

11. Students in a math class are divided into 8 equal groups with at least 3 students in each group for a project.

   a. Write an inequality to describe the possible numbers of students in each group.

   b. Use the Multiplication Property of Inequality to write an inequality to describe the possible numbers of students in the class.

Describe all numbers that satisfy *both* inequalities. Include a graph with your description.

12. $-3x < -9$ and $-3x < 9$

13. $\dfrac{2}{3}t \ge 4$ and $-\dfrac{3}{5}t \ge -6$

14. $3x < 12$ and $-3x < -3$

15. $\dfrac{y}{5} \le -2$ and $-\dfrac{y}{4} \ge 1$

Name_____ Date _____

4.7 Solving Two-Step Inequalities
For use with Exploration 4.7

Learning Target: Write and solve two-step inequalities.

Success Criteria:
- I can apply properties of inequality to generate equivalent inequalities.
- I can solve two-step inequalities using the basic operations.
- I can apply two-step inequalities to solve real-life problems.

---

1 EXPLORATION: Using Algebra Tiles to Solve Inequalities

Work with a partner.

a. What is being modeled by the algebra tiles below? What is the solution?

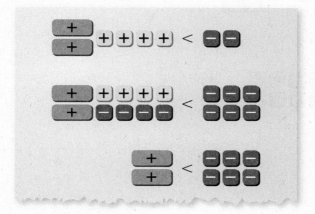

b. Use properties of inequality to solve the original inequality in part (a). How do your steps compare to the steps performed with algebra tiles?

4.7 **Solving Two-Step Inequalities** (continued)

c. Write the three inequalities modeled by the algebra tiles below. Then solve each inequality using algebra tiles. Check your answer using properties of inequality.

d. Explain how solving a two-step inequality is similar to solving a two-step equation.

4.7 Notetaking with Vocabulary

Vocabulary:

Notes:

4.7 Self-Assessment

Use the scale below to rate your understanding of the learning target and the success criteria.

1	*2*	*3*	*4*
I do not understand.	I can do it with help.	I can do it on my own.	I can teach someone else.

	Rating	Date
4.7 Solving Two-Step Inequalities		
Learning Target: Write and solve two-step inequalities.	1 2 3 4	
I can apply properties of inequality to generate equivalent inequalities.	1 2 3 4	
I can solve two-step inequalities using the basic operations.	1 2 3 4	
I can apply two-step inequalities to solve real-life problems.	1 2 3 4	

Name _____ Date _____

Solve the inequality. Graph the solution.

1. $2 - \frac{q}{3} > 6$

2. $7 \leq 0.5v + 10$

3. $-5(m - 2) > 30$

4. $-\frac{3}{2}(f + 6) \leq -6$

5. $10.5 < 1.5(p - 3)$

6. $30 \geq -7.5(w - 4.2)$

7. An RV park receives $300 per month from each residential site that is occupied as well as $2000 per month from their overnight sites. Write and solve an inequality to find the number of residential sites that must be occupied to make at least $14,000 in revenue each month.

8. Write and solve an inequality that represents the values of x for which the area of the rectangle will be at most 45 square meters.

4.5 m

$x + 3$

Solve the inequality. Graph the solution.

9. $12x - 5x - 4 \geq 60 - 8$

10. $4v + 6v + 3.2 < 6.8 - 9.2$

11. An animal shelter has fixed weekly expenses of $750. Each animal in the shelter costs an additional $6 a week.

   a. During the summer months, the total weekly expenses are at least $1170. Write and solve an inequality that represents the number of animals at the shelter for expenses to be at least $1170 a week.

   b. During the winter months, the total weekly expenses are at most $900. Write and solve an inequality that represents the number of animals at the shelter for expenses to be at most $900 a week.

   c. The cost for each animal has increased by $2. What will be the maximum weekly expenses during the winter month?

12. For what values of r will the area of the shaded region be greater than or equal to half of the area of the larger rectangle?

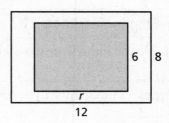

6 | 8

r

12

Name_____ Date _____

Chapter 4 Chapter Self-Assessment

Use the scale below to rate your understanding of the learning target and the success criteria.

1	**2**	**3**	**4**
I do not understand.	I can do it with help.	I can do it on my own.	I can teach someone else.

	Rating	Date
4.1 Solving Equations Using Addition or Subtraction		
Learning Target: Write and solve equations using addition or subtraction.	1 2 3 4	
I can apply the Addition and Subtraction Properties of Equality to produce equivalent equations.	1 2 3 4	
I can solve equations using addition or subtraction.	1 2 3 4	
I can apply equations involving addition or subtraction to solve real-life problems.	1 2 3 4	
4.2 Solving Equations Using Multiplication or Division		
Learning Target: Write and solve equations using multiplication or division.	1 2 3 4	
I can apply the Multiplication and Division Properties of Equality to produce equivalent equations.	1 2 3 4	
I can solve equations using multiplication or division.	1 2 3 4	
I can apply equations involving multiplication or division to solve real-life problems.	1 2 3 4	
4.3 Solving Two-Step Equations		
Learning Target: Write and solve two-step equations.	1 2 3 4	
I can apply properties of equality to produce equivalent equations.	1 2 3 4	
I can solve two-step equations using the basic operations.	1 2 3 4	
I can apply two-step equations to solve real-life problems.	1 2 3 4	

Chapter 4 — Chapter Self-Assessment (continued)

	Rating	Date
4.4 Writing and Graphing Inequalities		
Learning Target: Write inequalities and represent solutions of inequalities on number lines.	1 2 3 4	
I can write word sentences as inequalities.	1 2 3 4	
I can determine whether a value is a solution of an inequality.	1 2 3 4	
I can graph the solutions of inequalities.	1 2 3 4	
4.5 Solving Inequalities Using Addition or Subtraction		
Learning Target: Write and solve inequalities using addition or subtraction.	1 2 3 4	
I can apply the Addition and Subtraction Properties of Inequality to produce equivalent inequalities.	1 2 3 4	
I can solve inequalities using addition or subtraction.	1 2 3 4	
I can apply inequalities involving addition or subtraction to solve real-life problems.	1 2 3 4	
4.6 Solving Inequalities Using Multiplication or Division		
Learning Target: Write and solve inequalities using multiplication or division.	1 2 3 4	
I can apply the Multiplication and Division Properties of Inequality to produce equivalent inequalities.	1 2 3 4	
I can solve inequalities using multiplication or division.	1 2 3 4	
I can apply inequalities involving multiplication or division to solve real-life problems.	1 2 3 4	
4.7 Solving Two-Step Inequalities		
Learning Target: Write and solve two-step inequalities.	1 2 3 4	
I can apply properties of inequality to generate equivalent inequalities.	1 2 3 4	
I can solve two-step inequalities using the basic operations.	1 2 3 4	
I can apply two-step inequalities to solve real-life problems.	1 2 3 4	

Chapter 5 Review & Refresh

Simplify.

1. $\dfrac{3}{18}$

2. $\dfrac{4}{6}$

3. $\dfrac{12}{60}$

4. $\dfrac{14}{28}$

5. $\dfrac{16}{36}$

6. $\dfrac{40}{50}$

Are the fractions equivalent?

7. $\dfrac{3}{8} \overset{?}{=} \dfrac{6}{11}$

8. $\dfrac{4}{10} \overset{?}{=} \dfrac{16}{40}$

9. $\dfrac{22}{32} \overset{?}{=} \dfrac{11}{16}$

10. $\dfrac{63}{72} \overset{?}{=} \dfrac{7}{9}$

11. You see 58 birds while on a bird watching tour. Of those birds, you see 12 hawks. Write and simplify the fraction of birds you see that are hawks.

Chapter 5

Review & Refresh (continued)

Solve the equation. Check your solution.

12. $\dfrac{d}{12} = -4$

13. $-7 = \dfrac{x}{-3}$

14. $\dfrac{1}{8}n = 5$

15. $6a = -54$

16. $10 = -2k$

17. $2.7 = -0.9y$

18. $-23.4 = -13w$

19. $\dfrac{1}{15}z = 6$

20. You and three friends spend \$35 on tickets at the movies. Write and solve an equation to find the price p of one ticket.

5.1 Ratios and Ratio Tables
For use with Exploration 5.1

Learning Target: Understand ratios of rational numbers and use ratio tables to represent equivalent ratios.

Success Criteria:
- I can write and interpret ratios involving rational numbers.
- I can use various operations to create tables of equivalent ratios.
- I can use ratio tables to solve ratio problems.

1 EXPLORATION: Describing Ratio Relationships

Work with a partner. Use the recipe shown.

Chicken Soup

stewed tomatoes	9 ounces	chopped spinach	9 ounces
chicken broth	15 ounces	grated parmesan	5 tablespoons
chopped chicken	1 cup		

a. Identify several ratios in the recipe.

b. You halve the recipe. Describe your ratio relationships in part (a) using the new quantities. Is the relationship between the ingredients the same as in part (a)? Explain.

5.1   **Ratios and Ratio Tables** (continued)

2   **EXPLORATION:** Completing Ratio Tables

Work with a partner. Use the ratio tables shown.

x	5			
y	1			

x	$\dfrac{1}{4}$			
y	$\dfrac{1}{2}$			

a. Complete the first ratio table using multiple operations. Use the same operations to complete the second ratio table.

b. Are the ratios in the first table equivalent? the second table? Explain.

c. Do the strategies for completing ratio tables of whole numbers work for completing ratio tables of fractions? Explain your reasoning.

5.1 Notetaking with Vocabulary

Vocabulary:

Notes:

5.1 Self-Assessment

Use the scale below to rate your understanding of the learning target and the success criteria.

1	**2**	**3**	**4**
I do not understand.	I can do it with help.	I can do it on my own.	I can teach someone else.

	Rating	Date
5.1 Ratios and Ratio Tables		
Learning Target: Understand ratios of rational numbers and use ratio tables to represent equivalent ratios.	1 2 3 4	
I can write and interpret ratios involving rational numbers.	1 2 3 4	
I can use various operations to create tables of equivalent ratios.	1 2 3 4	
I can use ratio tables to solve ratio problems.	1 2 3 4	

Name _____ Date _____

5.1 Practice

Write the ratio as a fraction in simplest form.

1. 198 women to 110 men

2. 1000 songs : 2 megabytes

3. 26.1 miles : 3.6 hours

4. 12 completions to 28 attempts

Find the missing values in the ratio table. Then write the equivalent ratios.

5.

Coffee (ounces)	4	8		16
Cream (ounces)	$\frac{3}{8}$		$1\frac{1}{8}$	

6.

Yards	4			25
Seconds	6.4	10	15.6	

7. A water pipe leak floods 50 square feet every $\frac{1}{5}$ minute. What is the flooded area after 6 minutes?

8. You use $\frac{1}{32}$ milliliter of essential oils for every $\frac{3}{4}$ milliliter of avocado oil to make 150 milliliters of a solution.

   a. How much essential oils do you use? How much avocado oil do you use?

   b. You decide that you want to add coconut oil to the solution. You make the new mixture by adding $\frac{3}{16}$ milliliter of coconut oil for every $\frac{1}{32}$ milliliter of essential oils and $\frac{3}{4}$ milliliter of avocado oil. How much essential oils, avocado oil, and coconut oil do you use to make $15\frac{1}{2}$ milliliters of the new solution?

9. The ratio of white rice to water is 1 to $2\frac{1}{2}$. You have $\frac{2}{3}$ cup of rice. How much water do you need?

106 Big Ideas Math: Modeling Real Life Grade 7
Student Journal

Copyright © Big Ideas Learning, LLC
All rights reserved.

Name_____ Date _____

5.2 Rates and Unit Rates
For use with Exploration 5.2

Learning Target: Understand rates involving fractions and use unit rates to solve problems.

Success Criteria:
- I can find unit rates for rates involving fractions.
- I can use unit rates to solve rate problems.

1 EXPLORATION: Writing Rates

Work with a partner.

a. How many degrees does the minute hand on a clock move every 15 minutes? Write a rate that compares the number of degrees moved by the minute hand to the number of hours elapsed.

b. Can you use the rate in part (a) to determine how many degrees the minute hand moves in $\frac{1}{2}$ hour? Explain your reasoning.

5.2 Rates and Unit Rates (continued)

c. Write a rate that represents the number of degrees moved by the minute hand every hour. How can you use this rate to find the number of degrees moved by the minute hand in $2\frac{1}{2}$ hours?

d. Draw a clock with hour and minute hands. Draw another clock that shows the time after the minute hand moves 900°. How many degrees does the hour hand move in this time? in one hour? Explain your reasoning.

5.2 Notetaking with Vocabulary

Vocabulary:

Notes:

5.2 Self-Assessment

Use the scale below to rate your understanding of the learning target and the success criteria.

1	**2**	**3**	**4**
I do not understand.	I can do it with help.	I can do it on my own.	I can teach someone else.

	Rating	Date
5.2 Rates and Unit Rates		
Learning Target: Understand rates involving fractions and use unit rates to solve problems.	1 2 3 4	
I can find unit rates for rates involving fractions.	1 2 3 4	
I can use unit rates to solve rate problems.	1 2 3 4	

Name _____ Date _____

Find the unit rate.

1. $5.40 for 24 cans   2. $1.29 for 20 ounces   3. 50 meters in 27.5 seconds

4. Find the missing values in the ratio table. Then write the equivalent ratios.

Distance (Centimeters)	14	$\frac{3}{2}$		
Time (minute)	$\frac{4}{3}$		1	$\frac{1}{6}$

5. There are 16 bacteria in a beaker. Four hours later there are 228 bacteria in the beaker. What is the rate of change per hour in the number of bacteria?

6. The table shows nutritional information for three energy bars.

   a. Which has the most protein per calorie?

   b. Which has the least sugar per calorie?

Energy Bar	Calories	Protein	Fiber	Sugar
A	220	20 g	12 g	14 g
B	130	12 g	8 g	10 g
C	140	4 g	9 g	9 g

   c. Which has the highest rate of sugar to fiber?

   d. Compare Bar A with Bar B. Which nutritional item do you think has the highest ratio: calories, protein, fiber, or sugar?

   e. Calculate the ratios in part (d). Which one has the highest ratio?

7. The graph shows the cost of buying scoops of gelato.

   a. What does the point (4, 6) represent?

   b. What is the unit cost?

   c. What is the cost of 12 scoops?

   d. Explain how the graph would change if the unit rate was $1.75 per scoop.

   e. How would the coordinates of the point in part (a) change if the unit rate was $1.75 per scoop?

5.3 Identifying Proportional Relationships
For use with Exploration 5.3

Learning Target: Determine whether two quantities are in a proportional relationship.

Success Criteria:
- I can determine whether ratios form a proportion.
- I can explain how to determine whether quantities are proportional.
- I can distinguish between proportional and nonproportional situations.

1 EXPLORATION: Determining Proportional Relationships

Work with a partner.

a. You can paint 50 square feet of a surface every 40 minutes. How long does it take you to paint the mural shown? Explain how you found your answer.

b. The number of square feet you paint is *proportional* to the number of minutes it takes you. What do you think it means for a quantity to be *proportional* to another quantity?

5.3 **Identifying Proportional Relationships** (continued)

c. Assume your friends paint at the same rate as you. The table shows
how long it takes you and different numbers of friends to paint a fence.
Is *x* proportional to *y* in the table? Explain.

Painters, *x*	1	2	3	4
Hours, *y*	4	2	$\frac{4}{3}$	1

d. How long will it take you and four friends to paint the fence? Explain how
you found your answer.

Name_____ Date _____

5.3 Notetaking with Vocabulary

Vocabulary:

Notes:

5.3 Self-Assessment

Use the scale below to rate your understanding of the learning target and the success criteria.

1	**2**	**3**	**4**
I do not understand.	I can do it with help.	I can do it on my own.	I can teach someone else.

	Rating	Date
5.3 Identifying Proportional Relationships		
Learning Target: Determine whether two quantities are in a proportional relationship.	1 2 3 4	
I can determine whether ratios form a proportion.	1 2 3 4	
I can explain how to determine whether quantities are proportional.	1 2 3 4	
I can distinguish between proportional and nonproportional situations.	1 2 3 4	

5.3 Practice

Tell whether the ratios form a proportion.

1. $\dfrac{28.5}{42}, \dfrac{19}{28}$

2. $3.5 : 4$ and $11.9 : 13.6$

3. 124 to 98 and 315 to 225

Tell whether the rates form a proportion.

4. $24 for 16 burgers; $15 for 10 burgers

5. 10 used books for $4.50; 15 used books for $6.00

6. The ratio of pennies : nickels is proportional to the ratio of nickels : dimes, and to the ratio of dimes : quarters. If you have one penny and two nickels, how much money do you have?

7. The seventh-grade band has 15 drummers and 12 trumpet players. The eighth-grade band has 10 drummers and 8 trumpet players. Do the ratios form a proportion? Explain.

8. One mixture contains 6 fluid ounces of water and 10 fluid ounces of vinegar. A second mixture contains 9 fluid ounces of water and 12 fluid ounces of vinegar. Are the mixtures proportional? If not, how much water or vinegar would you add to the second mixture so that they are proportional?

9. A wholesale warehouse buys pairs of sandals to sell.

   a. The warehouse can purchase 5 pairs of sandals for $65. What is the cost rate?

   b. The warehouse can purchase 8 pairs of sandals for $96. What is the cost rate?

   c. The warehouse can purchase 10 pairs of sandals for $126.50 and will get one free pair. What is the cost rate?

   d. Are any of the cost rates proportional? Explain.

   e. Your buyer is to purchase 40 pairs of sandals. Use any combination of parts (a), (b), and (c) for your buyer to purchase the 40 pairs of sandals at the lowest possible cost.

Find the values of x and y so that the ratios form a proportion.

10. If $\dfrac{3}{7} = \dfrac{9}{21}$, then $\dfrac{3}{7+x} = \dfrac{9}{21+y}$.

11. If $\dfrac{16}{12} = \dfrac{20}{15}$, then $\dfrac{16}{12+x} = \dfrac{20}{15+y}$.

5.4 Writing and Solving Proportions
For use with Exploration 5.4

Learning Target: Use proportions to solve ratio problems.

Success Criteria: • I can solve proportions using various methods.
  • I can find a missing value that makes two ratios equivalent.
  • I can use proportions to represent and solve real-life problems.

1 EXPLORATION: Solving a Ratio Problem

Work with a partner. A train travels 50 miles every 40 minutes. To determine the number of miles the train travels in 90 minutes, your friend creates the following table.

Miles	50	x
Minutes	40	90

a. Explain how you can find the value of x.

b. Can you use the information in the table to write a proportion? If so, explain how you can use the proportion to find the value of x. If not, explain why not.

Name _____ Date _____

    c. If a train travels 30 miles every half hour. How far does the train travel in 2 hours?

    d. Share your results in part (c) with other groups. Compare and contrast methods used to solve the problem.

Name_____ Date _____

 5.4 **Notetaking with Vocabulary**

Vocabulary:

Notes:

5.4 **Self-Assessment**

Use the scale below to rate your understanding of the learning target and the success criteria.

1	**2**	**3**	**4**
I do not understand.	I can do it with help.	I can do it on my own.	I can teach someone else.

	Rating	Date
5.4 Writing and Solving Proportions		
Learning Target: Use proportions to solve ratio problems.	1 2 3 4	
I can solve proportions using various methods.	1 2 3 4	
I can find a missing value that makes two ratios equivalent.	1 2 3 4	
I can use proportions to represent and solve real-life problems.	1 2 3 4	

5.4 Practice

1. Describe and correct the error in writing the proportion.

2. There are 3 referees for every 16 players. Write a proportion that gives the number of referees r for 128 players.

	Day 1	Day 2
Length	3.1	15.5
Height	h	45

$$\frac{15.5}{h} = \frac{3.1}{45}$$

Solve the proportion.

3. $\dfrac{5}{12} = \dfrac{x}{36}$

4. $\dfrac{20}{3.4} = \dfrac{800}{y}$

5. $\dfrac{2.8}{r} = \dfrac{70}{3}$

6. You can buy 48 seashells for $15. How many seashells can you buy for $37.50?

7. You need 252 gift bags for an event. You found a gift bag that costs $6.50 for 21 bags. Your budget is $75. Is the gift bag within your budget? Justify your answer.

8. A recipe calls for $\frac{3}{4}$ cup of sugar and $\frac{1}{2}$ cup of brown sugar. You are reducing the recipe. You will use $\frac{1}{6}$ cup of brown sugar. How much sugar will you use?

9. A calculator has 50 keys in five colors: gray, black, blue, yellow, and green.

   a. There are 6 gray keys for every 7 blue keys. Write the possible ratios for gray to blue keys.

   b. There are 6 gray keys for every 11 black keys. Write the possible ratios for gray to black keys.

   c. There are 6 gray keys for every 11 black keys. Also, the number of black keys is 2 less than twice the number of gray keys. Use your answer to part (b) to determine how many gray keys and how many black keys there are.

   d. There is 1 yellow key for every 1 green key. How many keys of each color are there?

10. Give two possible pairs of values for p and q: $\dfrac{7}{10} = \dfrac{p}{q}$.

Name_____ Date _____

5.5 Graphs of Proportional Relationships
For use with Exploration 5.5

Learning Target: Represent proportional relationships using graphs and equations.

Success Criteria:
- I can determine whether quantities are proportional using a graph.
- I can find the unit rate of a proportional relationship using a graph.
- I can create equations to represent proportional relationships.

1 **EXPLORATION: Representing Relationships Graphically**

Work with a partner. The tables represent two different ways that red and blue food coloring are mixed.

Mixture 1	
Drops of Blue, x	Drops of Red, y
1	2
2	4
3	6
4	8

Mixture 2	
Drops of Blue, x	Drops of Red, y
0	2
2	4
4	6
6	8

a. Represent each table in the same coordinate plane. Which graph represents a proportional relationship? How do you know?

5.5   **Graphs of Proportional Relationships** (continued)

b. Find the unit rate of the proportional relationship. How is the unit rate shown on the graph?

c. What is the multiplicative relationship between x and y for the proportional relationship? How can you use this value to write an equation that relates y and x?

Name_____ Date _____

5.5 Notetaking with Vocabulary

Vocabulary:

Notes:

5.5 Self-Assessment

Use the scale below to rate your understanding of the learning target and the success criteria.

1	**2**	**3**	**4**
I do not understand.	I can do it with help.	I can do it on my own.	I can teach someone else.

	Rating	Date
5.5 Graphs of Proportional Relationships		
Learning Target: Represent proportional relationships using graphs and equations.	1 2 3 4	
I can determine whether quantities are proportional using a graph.	1 2 3 4	
I can find the unit rate of a proportional relationship using a graph.	1 2 3 4	
I can create equations to represent proportional relationships.	1 2 3 4	

Name _____ Date _____

5.5 Practice

Interpret each plotted point in the graph of the proportional relationship. Then identify the unit rate.

1.
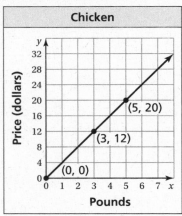

Chicken

Price (dollars) vs Pounds

(5, 20)
(3, 12)
(0, 0)

2.

Money

Earnings (dollars) vs Hours worked

(4, 100)
(2, 50)
(0, 0)

The graph of a proportional relationship passes through the given points. Find y.

3. $(4, 8), (1, y)$

4. $(3, 21), (1, y)$

5. $(1.5, 9), (1, y)$

6. $(3.5, 14), (1, y)$

7. Two classes have car washes to raise money for class trips. A portion of the earnings will pay for using the two locations for the car washes. The graph shows that the trip earnings of the two classes are proportional to the car wash earnings.

Class Trips

Trip earnings (dollars) vs Car wash earnings (dollars)

(20, 16) Class A
(20, 14)
Class B

a. Express the trip earnings rate for each class as a percent.

b. What trip earnings does Class A receive for earning $75 from the car wash?

c. How much less does Class B receive than Class A for earning $75 from the car wash?

The variables x and y are proportional. Use the values to find the constant of proportionality. Then write an equation that relates x and y.

8. When $y = 36$, $x = 18$.   **9.** When $y = 51$, $x = 34$.   **10.** When $y = 55$, $x = 10$.

11. Does the graph of every proportional relationship pass through the origin? Is every relationship whose graph passes through the origin a proportional relationship? Explain your reasoning.

5.6 Scale Drawings
For use with Exploration 5.6

Learning Target: Solve problems involving scale drawings.

Success Criteria:
- I can find an actual distance in a scale drawing.
- I can explain the meaning of scale and scale factor.
- I can use a scale drawing to find the actual lengths and areas of real-life objects.

1 EXPLORATION: Creating a Scale Drawing

Work with a partner. Several sections in a zoo are drawn on 1-centimeter grid paper as shown. Each centimeter in the drawing represents 4 meters.

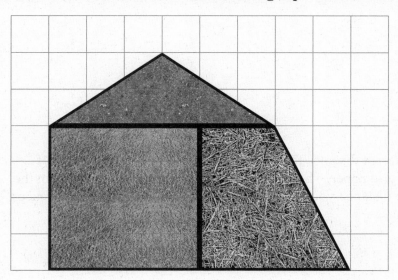

a. Describe the relationship between the lengths of the fences in the drawing and the actual side lengths of the fences.

5.6 **Scale Drawings** (continued)

b. Describe the relationship between the areas of the sections in the drawing and the actual areas of the sections.

c. Are the relationships in parts (a) and (b) the same? Explain your reasoning.

d. Choose a different distance to represent each centimeter on a piece of 1-centimeter grid paper. Then create a new drawing of the sections in the zoo using the distance you chose. Describe any similarities or differences in the drawings.

Name_____ Date_____

5.6 Notetaking with Vocabulary

Vocabulary:

Notes:

5.6 Self-Assessment

Use the scale below to rate your understanding of the learning target and the success criteria.

1	2	3	4
I do not understand.	I can do it with help.	I can do it on my own.	I can teach someone else.

	Rating	Date
5.6 Scale Drawings		
Learning Target: Solve problems involving scale drawings.	1 2 3 4	
I can find an actual distance in a scale drawing.	1 2 3 4	
I can explain the meaning of scale and scale factor.	1 2 3 4	
I can use a scale drawing to find the actual lengths and areas of real-life objects.	1 2 3 4	

5.6 Practice

1. In the actual blueprint of the bedroom suite, each square has a side length of $\frac{1}{2}$ inch.

   a. What are the dimensions of the bedroom suite?

   b. What are the dimensions of the bathroom?

   c. What is the length of the longest wall in the bedroom?

   d. What is the ratio of the perimeter of the closet to the perimeter of the bathroom?

   e. What is the ratio of the area of the closet to the area of the bathroom? How can you explain this by looking at the squares in each?

   f. All of the walls in the bedroom suite are covered with drywall. Which will cost the most to drywall – *the closet, the bathroom,* or *both are the same*?

   g. All of the floors in the bedroom suite are covered with the same tile. Which will cost the most to tile – *the closet, the bathroom* or *both are the same*?

Find the missing dimension. Use the scale 2 : 5.

Model	Actual
2. Depth: 10 km	Depth: ____ km
3. Length: 5 in.	Length: ____ in.
4. Length: ____ ft	Length: 24 ft
5. Diameter: ____ m	Diameter: 32.5 m

6. A scale factor is 1 : 8. Describe and correct the error in finding the model length that corresponds to 48 feet.

$$\times \quad \frac{1}{8} = \frac{48 \text{ ft}}{x \text{ ft}}$$
$$x = 384 \text{ ft}$$

Name_____ Date_____

Chapter Self-Assessment

Use the scale below to rate your understanding of the learning target and the success criteria.

1 I do not understand.　　**2** I can do it with help.　　**3** I can do it on my own.　　**4** I can teach someone else.

	Rating	Date
5.1 Ratios and Ratio Tables		
Learning Target: Understand ratios of rational numbers and use ratio tables to represent equivalent ratios.	1　2　3　4	
I can write and interpret ratios involving rational numbers.	1　2　3　4	
I can use various operations to create tables of equivalent ratios.	1　2　3　4	
I can use ratio tables to solve ratio problems.	1　2　3　4	
5.2 Rates and Unit Rates		
Learning Target: Understand rates involving fractions and use unit rates to solve problems.	1　2　3　4	
I can find unit rates for rates involving fractions.	1　2　3　4	
I can use unit rates to solve rate problems.	1　2　3　4	
5.3 Identifying Proportional Relationships		
Learning Target: Determine whether two quantities are in a proportional relationship.	1　2　3　4	
I can determine whether ratios form a proportion.	1　2　3　4	
I can explain how to determine whether quantities are proportional.	1　2　3　4	
I can distinguish between proportional and nonproportional situations.	1　2　3　4	

Name _____ Date _____

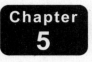
	Rating	Date
5.4 Writing and Solving Proportions		
Learning Target: Use proportions to solve ratio problems.	1　2　3　4	
I can solve proportions using various methods.	1　2　3　4	
I can find a missing value that makes two ratios equivalent.	1　2　3　4	
I can use proportions to represent and solve real-life problems.	1　2　3　4	
5.5 Graphs of Proportional Relationships		
Learning Target: Represent proportional relationships using graphs and equations.	1　2　3　4	
I can determine whether quantities are proportional using a graph.	1　2　3　4	
I can find the unit rate of a proportional relationship using a graph.	1　2　3　4	
I can create equations to represent proportional relationships.	1　2　3　4	
5.6 Scale Drawings		
Learning Target: Solve problems involving scale drawings.	1　2　3　4	
I can find an actual distance in a scale drawing.	1　2　3　4	
I can explain the meaning of scale and scale factor.	1　2　3　4	
I can use a scale drawing to find the actual lengths and areas of real-life objects.	1　2　3　4	

Name _____ Date _____

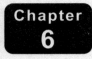

Write the percent as a fraction or mixed number in simplest form.

1. 25%

2. 65%

3. 110%

4. 250%

5. 15%

6. 6%

7. A store marks up a pair of sneakers 30%. Write the percent as a fraction or mixed number in simplest form.

Chapter 6 Review & Refresh (continued)

Write the fraction or mixed number as a percent.

8. $\dfrac{1}{5}$

9. $\dfrac{1}{4}$

10. $\dfrac{21}{25}$

11. $1\dfrac{2}{5}$

12. $2\dfrac{13}{20}$

13. $1\dfrac{1}{2}$

14. You own $\dfrac{3}{5}$ of the coins in a collection. What percent of the coins do you own?

Name_____ Date _____

6.1 Fractions, Decimals, and Percents
For use with Exploration 6.1

Learning Target: Rewrite fractions, decimals, and percents using different representations.

Success Criteria:
- I can write percents as decimals and decimals as percents.
- I can write fractions as decimals and percents.
- I can compare and order fractions, decimals, and percents.

1 EXPLORATION: Comparing Numbers in Different Forms

Work with a partner. Determine which number is greater. Explain your method.

a. 7% sales tax   or $\frac{1}{20}$ sales tax

b. 0.37 cup of flour   or $\frac{1}{3}$ cup of flour

c. $\frac{5}{8}$-inch wrench   or   0.375-inch wrench

d. $12\frac{3}{5}$ dollars   or   12.56 dollars

e. $5\frac{5}{6}$ fluid ounces   or   5.6 fluid ounces

6.1 **Fractions, Decimals, and Percents** (continued)

---

2 **EXPLORATION:** Ordering Fractions, Decimals, and Percents

Work with a partner and follow the steps below.

- Write five different numbers on individual slips of paper. Include at least one decimal, one fraction, and one percent.

- On a separate sheet of paper, create an answer key that shows your numbers written from least to greatest.

- Exchange slips of paper with another group and race to order the numbers from least to greatest. Then exchange answer keys to check your orders.

6.1 Notetaking with Vocabulary

Vocabulary:

Notes:

6.1 Self-Assessment

Use the scale below to rate your understanding of the learning target and the success criteria.

1	2	3	4
I do not understand.	I can do it with help.	I can do it on my own.	I can teach someone else.

	Rating	Date
6.1 Fractions, Decimals, and Percents		
Learning Target: Rewrite fractions, decimals, and percents using different representations.	1 2 3 4	
I can write percents as decimals and decimals as percents.	1 2 3 4	
I can write fractions as decimals and percents.	1 2 3 4	
I can compare and order fractions, decimals, and percents.	1 2 3 4	

6.1 Practice

Determine which number is greater. Explain your method.

1. $\frac{1}{4}, 22\%$　　　**2.** $\frac{5}{9}, 55\%$　　　**3.** $3.2, 32\%$　　　**4.** $99.9\%, 1$

Write the fraction as a decimal and a percent.

5. $\frac{13}{6}$　　　**6.** $\frac{25}{11}$　　　**7.** $\frac{1}{300}$　　　**8.** $\frac{3}{1000}$

Order the numbers from least to greatest. Explain your method.

9. $\frac{4}{3}, 1.333, 133.33\%, 1.334$　　　**10.** $81.8\%, 0.8182, 0.8\overline{2}, \frac{9}{11}$

11. Your band played for the local elementary school. After the concert, they surveyed the 2nd, 3rd, 4th, and 5th graders as to their interest in playing an instrument. The table gives the results of the survey.

Grade	2nd	3rd	4th	5th
Portion of Grade Interested in Playing an Instrument	0.52	$\frac{25}{36}$	61.24%	$0.572\overline{4}$

    a. What grade had the greatest portion of students interested in playing an instrument?

    b. What grade had the least portion of students interested in playing an instrument?

    c. How many times more is the portion of students in part (a) than the portion of students in part (b)?

    d. Did the interest in playing an instrument improve as students advanced from grade to grade, yes or no? Explain your answer.

12. At least 52% of the 25 students in a class brought their own lunch last month. What are the possible numbers of students in the class who brought their own lunch last month? Justify your answer.

13. Which do you prefer, writing a decimal as a percent or writing a fraction as a percent. Explain your answer.

Name_____ Date _____

Learning Target: Use the percent proportion to find missing quantities.

Success Criteria:
- I can write proportions to represent percent problems.
- I can solve a proportion to find a percent, a part, or a whole.

---

1 EXPLORATION: Using Percent Models

Work with a partner.

  a. Complete each model. Explain what each model represents.

6.2 **The Percent Proportion** (continued)

b. Use the models in part (a) to answer each question.

What number is 50% of 30?

15 is what percent of 75?

96 is $133\frac{1}{3}$% of what number?

c. How can you use ratio tables to check your answers in part (b)? How can you use proportions? Provide examples to support your reasoning.

d. Write a question different from those in part (b) that can be answered using one of the models in part (a). Trade questions with another group and find the solution.

Name_____ Date _____

 6.2 Notetaking with Vocabulary

Vocabulary:

Notes:

6.2 Self-Assessment

Use the scale below to rate your understanding of the learning target and
the success criteria.

1	*2*	*3*	*4*
I do not understand.	I can do it with help.	I can do it on my own.	I can teach someone else.

	Rating	Date
6.2 The Percent Proportion		
Learning Target: Use the percent proportion to find missing quantities.	1 2 3 4	
I can write proportions to represent percent problems.	1 2 3 4	
I can solve a proportion to find a percent, a part, or a whole.	1 2 3 4	

Name _____ Date _____

6.2 Practice

Write and solve a proportion to answer the question.

1. 55% of what number is 33?

2. What percent of 120 is 42?

3. 36 is 0.8% of what number?

4. 48 is what percent of 64?

5. Of the 360 runners at a 5-kilometer race, 20% are in the 35–39 age bracket. How many runners at the 5-kilometer race are in the 35–39 age bracket?

6. You pay $3.69 for a gallon of gasoline. This is 90% of the price of a gallon of gasoline one year ago. What was the price of a gallon of gasoline one year ago?

7. Describe and correct the error in using the percent proportion to answer the question below.

    "6 is 6.25% of what number?"

$$\cancel{}\quad \frac{a}{w} = \frac{p}{100}$$

$$\frac{6}{w} = \frac{0.0625}{100}$$

$$w = 9600$$

Write and solve a proportion to answer the question.

8. $\frac{7}{8}$ of the class likes chocolate milk. 70% of the class likes chocolate milk. How many students are in the class?

9. A pizza costs $7.20. This is 250% of the cost of a drink. What is the cost of the drink?

10. A reduced calorie recipe requires 72% of the normal amount of sugar. The normal amount of sugar is $\frac{3}{8}$ cup. How much sugar should you add to the reduced calorie recipe?

11. 1.4 is what percent of 1.12?

12. You earn a score of 86.8 on a standardized exam. Your score is 140% higher than your friend's score on the standardized exam. What is your friend's score?

13. 80% of a number is x. What is 40% of the number? Assume $x > 0$.

14. Answer each question. Assume $x > 0$.

    a. What is 35% of $90x$?

    b. What percent of $16x$ is $9x$?

6.3 The Percent Equation

For use with Exploration 6.3

Learning Target: Use the percent equation to find missing quantities.

Success Criteria:
- I can write equations to represent percent problems.
- I can use the percent equation to find a percent, a part, or a whole.

---

1 EXPLORATION: Using Percent Equations

Work with a partner.

a. The circle graph shows the number of votes received by each candidate during a school election. So far, only half of the students have voted. Find the percent of students who voted for each candidate. Explain your method.

Votes Received by Each Candidate

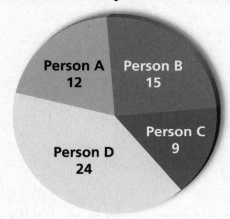

b. You have learned that $\dfrac{\text{part}}{\text{whole}}$ = percent. Solve the equation for the "part".

Explain your reasoning

6.3   **The Percent Equation** (continued)

c. The circle graph shows the final results
of the election after every student voted.
Use the equation you wrote in part (b) to
find the number of students who voted
for each candidate.

Final Results

d. Use a different method to check your answers in part (c). Which method do
you prefer? Explain.

Name_____ Date _____

6.3 Notetaking with Vocabulary

Vocabulary:

Notes:

6.3 Self-Assessment

Use the scale below to rate your understanding of the learning target and the success criteria.

1	**2**	**3**	**4**
I do not understand.	I can do it with help.	I can do it on my own.	I can teach someone else.

	Rating	Date
6.3 The Percent Equation		
Learning Target: Use the percent equation to find missing quantities.	1 2 3 4	
I can write equations to represent percent problems.	1 2 3 4	
I can use the percent equation to find a percent, a part, or a whole.	1 2 3 4	

Name _____ Date _____

6.3 Practice

Write and solve an equation to answer the question.

1. 27 is 0.5% of what number?

2. What number is 125% of 240?

3. 1.4% of what number is 28?

4. 27 is what percent of 72?

5. During a given month, there was a total of 23.6 inches of rain. This was 250% of the average rainfall for that month. What is the average rainfall for that month?

6. To maintain an acceptable level of chlorine in your pool, you add 1.4 gallons of chlorine. This is 0.007% of the amount of water in your pool. How many gallons of water are in your pool?

7. You must attend a minimum of 85% of the practices in order to play in the playoffs. You have made 37 of the 42 practices. Will you be able to play in the playoffs?

8. You are in charge of the seventh-grade graduation dinner. The table shows the results of a survey of students' meal preferences.

Choice	Percent
Chicken Nuggets	25%
Spaghetti	?
Pizza	45%
Fish Sticks	?

   a. 144 students chose pizza. How many students responded to the survey?

   b. How many students chose chicken nuggets?

   c. The number of students choosing fish sticks was 50% of the number of students choosing spaghetti. How many students chose fish sticks?

   d. How many students chose spaghetti?

9. What is 15% of 40% of $180?

10. There are 15 copies of a popular CD left to be sold in a store. This is between 1% and 1.5% of the original number of copies of the CD in the store. The original number of CDs was between what two numbers?

11. Tell whether the statement is *true* or *false*. Explain your reasoning.

   If A is 45% of B, then the ratio of $A : B$ is 9 : 20.

6.4 Percents of Increase and Decrease
For use with Exploration 6.4

Learning Target: Find percents of change in quantities.

Success Criteria:
- I can explain the meaning of percent of change.
- I can find the percent of increase or decrease in a quantity.
- I can find the percent error of a quantity.

---

1 EXPLORATION: Exploring Percent of Change

Work with a partner.

Each year in the Columbia River Basin, adult salmon swim upriver to streams to lay eggs.

To go up river, the adult salmon use fish ladders. But to go down river, the young salmon must pass through several dams.

At one time, there were electric turbines at each of the eight dams on the main stem of the Columbia and Snake Rivers. About 88% of the young salmon pass through a single dam unharmed.

a. One thousand young salmon pass through a dam. How many pass through unharmed?

b. One thousand young salmon pass through the river basin. How many pass through all 8 dams unharmed?

6.4 **Percents of Increase and Decrease** (continued)

c. By what percent does the number of young salmon *decrease* when passing through a single dam?

d. Describe a similar real-life situation in which a quantity *increases* by a constant percent each time an event occurs.

6.4 Notetaking with Vocabulary

Vocabulary:

Notes:

6.4 Self-Assessment

Use the scale below to rate your understanding of the learning target and the success criteria.

1	2	3	4
I do not understand.	I can do it with help.	I can do it on my own.	I can teach someone else.

	Rating	Date
6.4 Percents of Increase and Decrease		
Learning Target: Find percents of change in quantities.	1 2 3 4	
I can explain the meaning of percent of change.	1 2 3 4	
I can find the percent of increase or decrease in a quantity.	1 2 3 4	
I can find the percent error of a quantity.	1 2 3 4	

6.4 Practice

Identify the percent of change as an *increase* or a *decrease*. Then find the percent of change. Round to the nearest tenth of a percent if necessary.

1. 3.2 kilograms to 2.4 kilograms

2. 41 euros to 85 euros

3. $\frac{2}{7}$ to $\frac{4}{7}$

4. $\frac{5}{6}$ to $\frac{1}{3}$

5. Last month you swam the 50-meter freestyle in 28.38 seconds. Today you swam it in 27.33 seconds. What is your percent of change? Round to the nearest tenth of a percent if necessary.

6. Last week 1200 burgers were served at a restaurant.

   a. This week 1176 burgers were served. What is the percent of change?

   b. Use the percent of change from part (a) to predict the number of burgers served next week. Round to the nearest whole number if necessary.

7. The price of a share of a stock was $37.50 yesterday.

   a. Today there was a price decrease of 4%. What is today's price?

   b. Based on today's price in part (a), what percent of change is needed to bring the price back up to $37.50? Round to the nearest tenth of a percent if necessary.

8. The table shows the membership of two scout troops.

Year	Troop A	Troop B
2010	14	21
2011	16	24

   a. What is the percent of change in membership from 2010 to 2011 for Troop A? Round to the nearest tenth of a percent if necessary.

   b. What is the percent of change in membership from 2010 to 2011 for Troop B? Round to the nearest tenth of a percent if necessary.

   c. Which troop has the better record in terms of the number of new members?

   d. Which troop has the better record in terms of the percent of change in membership?

6.5 Discounts and Markups
For use with Exploration 6.5

Learning Target: Solve percent problems involving discounts and markups.

Success Criteria:
- I can use percent models to solve problems involving discounts and markups.
- I can write and solve equations to solve problems involving discounts and markups.

1 EXPLORATION: Comparing Discounts

Work with a partner.

a. The same pair of earrings is on sale at three stores. Which store has the best price? Use the percent models to justify your answer.

Store A:	Store B:	Store C:
Regular Price: $45	Regular Price: $49	Regular Price: $39
40% off	50% off	20% off

6.5   **Discounts and Markups** (continued)

b. You buy the earrings on sale for 30% off at a different store. You pay
$22.40. What was the original price of the earrings? Use the percent model
to justify your answer.

Percent
0%   100%

0   22.40   Original
Dollars   Price

c. You sell the earrings in part (b) to a friend for 60% more than what you
paid. What is the selling price? Use a percent model to justify your answer.

6.5 Notetaking with Vocabulary

Vocabulary:

Notes:

6.5 Self-Assessment

Use the scale below to rate your understanding of the learning target and the success criteria.

1	2	3	4
I do not understand.	I can do it with help.	I can do it on my own.	I can teach someone else.

	Rating	Date
6.5 Discounts and Markups		
Learning Target: Solve percent problems involving discounts and markups.	1 2 3 4	
I can use percent models to solve problems involving discounts and markups.	1 2 3 4	
I can write and solve equations to solve problems involving discounts and markups.	1 2 3 4	

6.5 Practice

Find the original price, discount, sale price, selling price, markup, or cost to store. Round to the nearest penny if necessary.

1. Original price: $130

   Discount: 45%

   Sale price: ____

2. Original price: $500

   Discount: ____

   Sale price: $175

3. Original price: ____

   Discount: 5%

   Sale price: $68.40

4. Cost to store: $1600

   Markup: 33%

   Selling price: ____

5. Cost to store: $65

   Markup: ____

   Selling price: $91

6. Cost to store: ____

   Markup: 25%

   Selling price: $437.50

7. You are buying shoes online. The selling price is $29.99. Round to the nearest penny if necessary.

   a. The sales tax is 6.5%. What is the total cost?

   b. The cost of shipping is 15% of the total cost. What is the total cost plus shipping?

   c. If the total cost plus shipping is greater than $35, then you receive a 10% discount off the original selling price. Do you qualify? If so, what is the new total cost plus shipping?

8. You have a coupon for $15 off a video game. You can use it on 2 separate days.

   a. On Monday, you buy a video game. The discounted price of your video game is $22.99. What is the original price of the game?

   b. What is the percent of the discount to the nearest percent for the video game that you purchased on Monday?

   c. On Thursday, you buy another video game. The discounted price of your video game is $12.99. What is the original price of the game?

   d. What is the percent of the discount to the nearest percent for the video game that you purchased on Thursday?

6.6 Simple Interest
For use with Exploration 6.6

Learning Target: Understand and apply the simple interest formula.

Success Criteria:
- I can explain the meaning of simple interest.
- I can use the simple interest formula to solve problems.

1 EXPLORATION: Understanding Simple Interest

Work with a partner. You deposit $150 in an account that earns 6% *simple interest per year*. You do not make any other deposits or withdrawals. The table shows the balance of the account at the end of each year.

Years	Balance
0	$150
1	$159
2	$168
3	$177
4	$186
5	$195
6	$204

a. Describe any patterns you see in the account balance.

b. How is the amount of interest determined each year?

Name _____ Date _____

6.6 **Simple Interest** (continued)

c. How can you find the amount of simple interest earned when you are given an initial amount, an interest rate, and a period of time?

d. You deposit $150 in a different account that earns simple interest. The table shows the balance of the account each year. What is the interest rate of the account? What is the balance after 10 years?

Years	0	1	2	3
Balance	$150	$165	$180	$195

6.6 Notetaking with Vocabulary

Vocabulary:

Notes:

6.6 Self-Assessment

Use the scale below to rate your understanding of the learning target and the success criteria.

1	**2**	**3**	**4**
I do not understand.	I can do it with help.	I can do it on my own.	I can teach someone else.

	Rating	Date
6.6 Simple Interest		
Learning Target: Understand and apply the simple interest formula.	1 2 3 4	
I can explain the meaning of simple interest.	1 2 3 4	
I can use the simple interest formula to solve problems.	1 2 3 4	

Name _____ Date _____

An account earns simple interest. (a) Find the interest earned. (b) Find the balance of the account.

1. $2600 at 3.2% for 4 years

2. $75,000 at 8.5% for 3 months

Find the annual interest rate or find the amount of time.

3. $I = \$41.80$, $P = \$440$, $t = 2$ years

4. $I = \$893.75$, $P = \$5500$, $t = 30$ months

5. $I = \$9.90$, $P = \$360$, $r = 5.5\%$

6. $I = \$2064$, $P = \$10,000$, $r = 6.88\%$

Find the amount paid for the loan.

7. You borrow $20,000 to purchase a car. The interest rate is 7.5%. The loan is for 10 years. What is the total amount paid? How much would the payment be each month?

8. You invest $6000 in a restaurant. The investment has a return of 12%. How much do you receive for your investment after 30 months?

9. You deposit $2000 in an account. The account earns $120 simple interest in 8 months. What is the annual interest rate?

10. You put money in two different accounts for one year each. The total simple interest for the two accounts is $140. You earn 6% interest on the first account, in which you deposited $1000. You deposited $800 in the second account. What is the annual interest rate for the second account?

11. You deposit $1200 in an account.

    a. The account earns 2.7% simple interest rate. What is the balance of the account after 3 months?

    b. The interest rate changes, and your new balance now earns 2% simple interest rate. What is the balance of the account after the next 6 months? Round to the nearest penny if necessary.

    c. The interest rate changes again, and your new balance now earns 2.6% simple interest rate. What is the balance of the account after an additional 3 months? Round to the nearest penny if necessary.

    d. How much did the account earn in simple interest for the year?

    e. Based on the interest in part (d), what is the actual simple interest rate for the year? Round to the nearest tenth of a percent.

12. You purchase a new guitar and take out a loan for $450. You have 18 equal monthly payments of $28 each. What is the simple interest rate for the loan? Round to the nearest tenth of a percent if necessary.

Name_____ Date _____

Chapter Self-Assessment

Use the scale below to rate your understanding of the learning target and the success criteria.

1	**2**	**3**	**4**
I do not understand.	I can do it with help.	I can do it on my own.	I can teach someone else.

	Rating	Date
6.1 Fractions, Decimals, and Percents		
Learning Target: Rewrite fractions, decimals, and percents using different representations.	1 2 3 4	
I can write percents as decimals and decimals as percents.	1 2 3 4	
I can write fractions as decimals and percents.	1 2 3 4	
I can compare and order fractions, decimals, and percents.	1 2 3 4	
6.2 The Percent Proportion		
Learning Target: Use the percent proportion to find missing quantities.	1 2 3 4	
I can write proportions to represent percent problems.	1 2 3 4	
I can solve a proportion to find a percent, a part, or a whole.	1 2 3 4	
6.3 The Percent Equation		
Learning Target: Use the percent equation to find missing quantities.	1 2 3 4	
I can write equations to represent percent problems.	1 2 3 4	
I can use the percent equation to find a percent, a part, or a whole.	1 2 3 4	

Chapter Self-Assessment (continued)

	Rating	Date
6.4 Percents of Increase and Decrease		
Learning Target: Find percents of change in quantities.	1 2 3 4	
I can explain the meaning of percent of change.	1 2 3 4	
I can find the percent of increase or decrease in a quantity.	1 2 3 4	
I can find the percent error of a quantity.	1 2 3 4	
6.5 Discounts and Markups		
Learning Target: Solve percent problems involving discounts and markups.	1 2 3 4	
I can use percent models to solve problems involving discounts and markups.	1 2 3 4	
I can write and solve equations to solve problems involving discounts and markups.	1 2 3 4	
6.6 Simple Interest		
Learning Target: Understand and apply the simple interest formula.	1 2 3 4	
I can explain the meaning of simple interest.	1 2 3 4	
I can use the simple interest formula to solve problems.	1 2 3 4	

Name_____ Date _____

Write the ratio in simplest form.

1. bats to baseballs

2. bows to gift boxes

3. hammers to screwdrivers

4. apples to bananas

5. There are 100 students in the sixth grade. There are 15 sixth-grade teachers. What is the ratio of teachers to students?

Chapter 7 **Review & Refresh** (continued)

Write the ratio in simplest form.

6. golf balls to total number of balls

7. rulers to total pieces of equipment

8. apples to total number of fruit

9. small fish to total number of fish

10. There are 24 flute players and 18 trumpet players in the band. Write the ratio of trumpet players to total number of trumpet players and flute players.

7.1 Probability

For use with Exploration 7.1

Learning Target: Understand how the probability of an event indicates its likelihood.

Success Criteria:
- I can identify possible outcomes of an experiment.
- I can use probability and relative frequency to describe the likelihood of an event.
- I can use relative frequency to make predictions.

---

1 EXPLORATION: Determining Likelihood

Work with a partner. Use the spinners shown.

a. For each spinner, determine which numbers you are more likely to spin and which numbers you are less likely to spin. Explain your reasoning.

7.1 **Probability** (continued)

b. Spin each spinner 20 times (*) and record your results in two tables. Do the data support your answers in part (a)? Explain why or why not?

Spinner 1	
Number	**Frequency**
1	
2	
3	
4	
5	
6	

Spinner 2	
Number	**Frequency**
1	
2	
3	
4	
5	
6	

c. How can you use percents to describe the likelihood of spinning each number? Explain.

(*) Spinners are available in the back of the Student Journal.

7.1 Notetaking with Vocabulary

Vocabulary:

Notes:

7.1 Self-Assessment

Use the scale below to rate your understanding of the learning target and the success criteria.

1	**2**	**3**	**4**
I do not understand.	I can do it with help.	I can do it on my own.	I can teach someone else.

	Rating	Date
7.1 Probability		
Learning Target: Understand how the probability of an event indicates its likelihood.	1 2 3 4	
I can identify possible outcomes of an experiment.	1 2 3 4	
I can use probability and relative frequency to describe the likelihood of an event.	1 2 3 4	
I can use relative frequency to make predictions.	1 2 3 4	

7.1 Practice

You randomly choose one shape from the bag.
(a) Find the number of ways the event can occur.
(b) Find the favorable outcomes of the event.

1. Choosing a triangle

2. Choosing a star

3. Choosing *not* a square

4. Choosing *not* a circle

5. There are 12 cats and 7 dogs at the Humane Society.

   a. In how many ways can the first customer randomly choose a cat? Explain.

   b. What is the probability the second customer randomly chooses a dog?

   c. What is the probability the third customer randomly chooses a dog? Explain.

   d. What is the probability the fourth customer randomly chooses a dog or a cat?

   e. When the fifth customer arrives, what is the probability of randomly choosing a dog if the fourth customer chose a cat?

Describe the likelihood of the event from the given information.

6. The school bus arrives late $\frac{2}{7}$ of the time. The school bus arrives on time.

7. The probability that it rains during a hurricane is 1. It rains during a hurricane.

8. There is an 85% chance that you will go to the concert. You do not go to the concert.

9. A store has 30 blue pens, 18 black pens, and 12 red pens in stock. You buy 3 blue pens, 9 black pens, and 3 red pens. Find the probability of each event before and after your purchase. Then describe how your purchase affects the probability of each event.

   a. Randomly choosing a blue pen.

   b. Randomly choosing a black pen.

   c. Randomly choosing a red pen.

7.2 Experimental and Theoretical Probability
For use with Exploration 7.2

Learning Target: Develop probability models using experimental and theoretical probability.

Success Criteria:
- I can explain the meanings of experimental probability and theoretical probability.
- I can find experimental and theoretical probabilities.
- I can use probability to make predictions.

1   EXPLORATION: Conducting Experiments

Work with a partner. Conduct the following experiments and find the relative frequencies.

Experiment 1

- Flip a quarter 25 times and record whether each flip lands heads up or tails up.

Experiment 2

- Toss a thumbtack onto a table 25 times and record whether each toss lands point up or on its side.

7.2   **Experimental and Theoretical Probability** (continued)

a. Combine your results with those of your classmates. Do the relative frequencies change? What do you notice?

b. Everyone in your school conducts each experiment and you combine the results. How do you expect the relative frequencies to change? Explain.

c. How many times in 1000 flips do you expect a quarter to land heads up? How many times in 1000 tosses to you expect a thumbtack to land point up? Explain your reasoning.

d. In a *uniform probability model*, each outcome is equally likely to occur. Can you use a uniform probability model to describe either experiment? Explain.

7.2 Notetaking with Vocabulary

Vocabulary:

Notes:

7.2 Self-Assessment

Use the scale below to rate your understanding of the learning target and the success criteria.

1	2	3	4
I do not understand.	I can do it with help.	I can do it on my own.	I can teach someone else.

	Rating	Date
7.2 Experimental and Theoretical Probability		
Learning Target: Develop probability models using experimental and theoretical probability.	1　2　3　4	
I can explain the meanings of experimental probability and theoretical probability.	1　2　3　4	
I can find experimental and theoretical probabilities.	1　2　3　4	
I can use probability to make predictions.	1　2　3　4	

Name _____ Date _____

7.2 Practice

You have four sticks. Two sticks have one blue
side and one pink side. One stick has 2 blue sides.
One stick has 2 pink sides. You throw the sticks
20 times and record the results. Use the table to
find the experimental probability of the event.

Outcome	Frequency
3 blue, 1 pink	7
2 blue, 2 pink	9
1 blue, 3 pink	4

1. tossing 1 pink and 3 blue

2. tossing the same number of blue and pink

3. *not* tossing 3 pink

4. tossing at most 2 blue

5. You check 30 containers of yogurt. Seven of them have an expiration date
   within the next 3 days.

   a. What is the experimental probability that a container of yogurt will have
      an expiration date within the next 3 days?

   b. Out of 120 containers of yogurt, how many would you expect to have an
      expiration date within the next 3 days? Explain.

6. You flip 3 coins 50 times, and flipping 3 tails occurs 6 times, flipping 3 heads
   occurs 7 times.

   a. What is the theoretical probability that you flip 3 heads?

   b. What is the theoretical probability that you flip less than 3 heads?

   c. What is the experimental probability that you flip 3 heads?

   d. What is the experimental probability that you flip 3 tails?

   e. How many times would you expect to flip 3 tails out of 200 trials of
      flipping 3 coins? Explain.

7. Each letter of the alphabet is printed on an index card. After removing the
   cards that spell the word "vowel," what is the theoretical probability of
   randomly choosing a vowel? Explain.

8. There are 12 cats and 8 dogs in the pet store.

   a. What is the theoretical probability that a randomly chosen pet is a cat?

   b. Two days later, there are half as many cats in the pet store. The
      theoretical probability that a randomly chosen pet is a cat is half that of
      two days earlier. How many dogs are in the pet store two days later?

7.3 Compound Events
For use with Exploration 7.3

Learning Target: Find sample spaces and probabilities of compound events.

Success Criteria:
- I can find the sample space of two or more events.
- I can find the total number of possible outcomes of two or more events.
- I can find probabilities of compound events.

---

1 EXPLORATION: Comparing Combination Locks

Work with a partner. You are buying a combination lock. You have three choices.

a. One lock has 3 wheels. Each wheel is numbered from 0 to 9. How many possible outcomes are there for each wheel? How many possible combinations are there?

b. How can you use the number of possible outcomes on each wheel to determine the number of possible combinations?

7.3   **Compound Events** (continued)

   c. Another lock has one wheel numbered from 0 to 39. Each combination uses
     a sequence of three numbers. How many possible combinations are there?

   d. Another lock has 4 wheels as described. How many possible combinations
     are there?

     Wheel 1: 0–9

     Wheel 2: A–J

     Wheel 3: K–T

     Wheel 4: 0–9

   e. For which lock are you least likely to guess the combination? Why?

Name_____ Date _____

7.3 Notetaking with Vocabulary

Vocabulary:

Notes:

7.3 Self-Assessment

Use the scale below to rate your understanding of the learning target and the success criteria.

1	**2**	**3**	**4**
I do not understand.	I can do it with help.	I can do it on my own.	I can teach someone else.

	Rating	Date
7.3 Compound Events		
Learning Target: Find sample spaces and probabilities of compound events.	1　2　3　4	
I can find the sample space of two or more events.	1　2　3　4	
I can find the total number of possible outcomes of two or more events.	1　2　3　4	
I can find probabilities of compound events.	1　2　3　4	

Name _____ Date _____

7.3 Practice

Use a tree diagram to find the sample space and the total number of possible outcomes.

1.

Game	
Coin	Quarter, Dime, Nickel, Penny
Card	King, Queen, Jack

Use the Fundamental Counting Principle to find the total number of possible outcomes.

2.

Sandwich	
Bread	Italian, Wheat
Meat	Ham, Roast Beef, Salami
Cheese	American, Provolone, Swiss

3. Your computer password contains six characters. Each character is either a number or a letter. How many different passwords are possible? If numbers and letters cannot be used more than once, how many passwords are possible?

4. To win the jackpot you must match five numbers from 1 to 40. What is the probability that you will win the jackpot?

5. You need to hang seven pictures in a straight line.

   a. In how many ways can this be accomplished?

   b. If the picture of your great-grandfather must be in the middle, how many ways can the seven pictures be hung? Explain.

6. A license plate must contain two letters followed by four digits. How many license plates are possible? If the rule changed to five digits instead of four digits, how many more license plates would be possible?

Name_____ Date _____

Simulations
For use with Exploration 7.4

Learning Target: Design and use simulations to find probabilities of compound events.

Success Criteria:
- I can design a simulation to model a real-life situation.
- I can recognize favorable outcomes in a simulation.
- I can use simulations to find experimental probabilities.

1 EXPLORATION: Using a Simulation

Work with a partner. A basketball player makes 80% of her free throw attempts.

a. Is she likely to make at least two of her next three free throws? Explain your reasoning.

b. The table shows 30 randomly generated numbers from 0 to 999. Let each number represent three shots. How can you use the digits of these numbers to represent made shots and missed shots?

838	617	282	341	785
747	332	279	082	716
937	308	800	994	689
198	025	853	591	813
672	289	518	649	540
865	631	227	004	840

7.4 **Simulations** (continued)

c. Use the table to estimate the probability that of her next three free throws, she makes

- exactly two free throws.

- at most one free throw.

- at least two free throws.

- at least two free throws in a row.

d. The experiment used in parts (b) and (c) is called a *simulation*. Another player makes $\frac{3}{5}$ of her free throws. Describe a simulation that can be used to estimate the probability that she makes three of her next four free throws.

Name_____ Date_____

 7.4 **Notetaking with Vocabulary**

Vocabulary:

Notes:

 7.4 **Self-Assessment**

Use the scale below to rate your understanding of the learning target and the success criteria.

1	**2**	**3**	**4**
I do not understand.	I can do it with help.	I can do it on my own.	I can teach someone else.

		Rating	Date
7.4 Simulations			
Learning Target: Design and use simulations to find probabilities of compound events.		1 2 3 4	
I can design a simulation to model a real-life situation.		1 2 3 4	
I can recognize favorable outcomes in a simulation.		1 2 3 4	
I can use simulations to find experimental probabilities.		1 2 3 4	

Name_____ Date _____

7.4 Practice

A medicine is effective on 70% of patients. The table shows 30 randomly generated numbers from 0 to 999. Use the table to estimate the probability of the event.

028	837	618	205	984
724	301	249	946	925
042	113	696	985	632
312	085	997	198	398
117	240	853	373	597
606	077	016	012	695

1. The medicine is effective on at least two of the next three patients.

2. The medicine is effective on none of the next three patients.

Design and use a simulation to find the experimental probability.

3. A bowler hits the head pin 90% of the time that all ten pins are standing. What is the experimental probability that the bowler hits the head pin exactly four of the next five times that all ten pins are standing?

4. In your garden, 40% of your pineapple plants produce a pineapple each year. What is the experimental probability that at most two of the three pineapple plants produce a pineapple this year? Explain.

5. A fitness center randomly selects one of five free gifts to send to each new customer. Gifts include a workout towel, a water bottle, a heart monitor, a T-shirt, and a gift card to the marketplace. What is the experimental probability that for the next two customers, one receives a heart monitor and one receives a gift card to the marketplace? Explain.

Design and use a simulation with number cubes to estimate the probability.

6. Your younger sibling will finish his or her dinner plate two out of every six dinners. Estimate the probability that at least two of the next three dinner plates are finished. Explain.

7. You win your favorite video game $\frac{5}{6}$ of the time. Estimate the probability that you will win your favorite video game exactly three of the next four times you play the game. Explain.

Name_____ Date_____

Chapter 7 Chapter Self-Assessment

Use the scale below to rate your understanding of the learning target and the success criteria.

1	2	3	4
I do not understand.	I can do it with help.	I can do it on my own.	I can teach someone else.

	Rating	Date
7.1 Probability		
Learning Target: Understand how the probability of an event indicates its likelihood.	1 2 3 4	
I can identify possible outcomes of an experiment.	1 2 3 4	
I can use probability and relative frequency to describe the likelihood of an event.	1 2 3 4	
I can use relative frequency to make predictions.	1 2 3 4	
7.2 Experimental and Theoretical Probability		
Learning Target: Develop probability models using experimental and theoretical probability.	1 2 3 4	
I can explain the meanings of experimental probability and theoretical probability.	1 2 3 4	
I can find experimental and theoretical probabilities.	1 2 3 4	
I can use probability to make predictions.	1 2 3 4	
7.3 Compound Events		
Learning Target: Find sample spaces and probabilities of compound events.	1 2 3 4	
I can find the sample space of two or more events.	1 2 3 4	
I can find the total number of possible outcomes of two or more events.	1 2 3 4	
I can find probabilities of compound events.	1 2 3 4	

Chapter 7

Chapter Self-Assessment (continued)

	Rating				Date
7.4 Simulations					
Learning Target: Design and use simulations to find probabilities of compound events.	1	2	3	4	
I can design a simulation to model a real-life situation.	1	2	3	4	
I can recognize favorable outcomes in a simulation.	1	2	3	4	
I can use simulations to find experimental probabilities.	1	2	3	4	

Name_____ Date_____

Review & Refresh

Find the mean of the data.

1. 15, 21, 10, 18, 26, 23, 18, 20, 21, 19, 25, 22

2. 76, 105, 98, 198, 103, 84, 112, 88, 101, 81, 92

3. 47.5, 47.3, 47.2, 47.4, 47.9, 47.5, 47.1, 47.6, 47.7

4. Identify any outliers in Exercises 1–3. Describe the effect of the outlier on the mean.

Chapter 8 Review & Refresh (continued)

Find the median, first quartile, third quartile, and interquartile range of the data.

5. 45, 68, 59, 38, 21, 26, 58, 46, 33, 41, 52, 51, 25

6. 187, 225, 174, 179, 231, 208, 110, 200, 194, 215, 199, 212

7. 2.6, 4.9, 1.4, 1.7, 2.3, 9.4, 3.8, 3.5, 7.6, 4.4, 5.0, 3.1, 2.6, 6.8, 9.1

8. Use the interquartile range to identify any outliers in Exercises 5–7.

8.1 Samples and Populations
For use with Exploration 8.1

Learning Target: Understand how to use random samples to make conclusions about a population.

Success Criteria:
- I can explain why a sample is biased or unbiased.
- I can explain why conclusions made from a biased sample may not be valid.
- I can use an unbiased sample to make a conclusion about a population.

---

1 EXPLORATION: Using Samples of Populations

Work with a partner. You want to make conclusions about the favorite extracurricular activities of students at your school.

  a. Identify the population. Then identify five samples of the population.

  b. When a sample is selected *at random*, each member of the population is equally likely to be selected. Are any of the samples in part (a) selected at random? Explain your reasoning.

8.1 **Samples and Populations** (continued)

c. How are the samples below different? Is each conclusion valid? Explain your reasoning.

You ask 20 members of the school band about their favorite activity. The diagram shows the results. You conclude that band is the favorite activity of 70% of the students in your school.

Favorite Activity

You ask every eighth student who enters the school about their favorite activity. One student says glee club for every nine that name a different activity. You conclude that glee club is the favorite activity of 10% of the students in your school.

d. Write a survey question about a topic that interests you. How can you choose people to survey so that you can use the results to make a valid conclusion?

8.1 Notetaking with Vocabulary

Vocabulary:

Notes:

8.1 Self-Assessment

Use the scale below to rate your understanding of the learning target and the success criteria.

1	**2**	**3**	**4**
I do not understand.	I can do it with help.	I can do it on my own.	I can teach someone else.

	Rating	Date
8.1 Samples and Populations		
Learning Target: Understand how to use random samples to make conclusions about a population.	1 2 3 4	
I can explain why a sample is biased or unbiased.	1 2 3 4	
I can explain why conclusions made from a biased sample may not be valid.	1 2 3 4	
I can use an unbiased sample to make a conclusion about a population.	1 2 3 4	

8.1 Practice

1. You want to know the number of fans at the Miami Dolphins and Dallas Cowboys game that think the Dolphins will win. You survey 50 fans with season tickets for the Dolphins.

    a. What is the population of your survey?

    b. What is the sample of your survey?

    c. Is the sample biased or unbiased? Explain.

2. Which sample is better for making an estimate? Explain.

Estimate the number of families in your town with two or more children.	
Sample A	A random sample of 10 families living near your home
Sample B	A random sample of 10 families living in your town

Determine whether you would survey the population or a sample. Explain.

3. You want to know the favorite clothing store of the students at your school.

4. You want to know the favorite topic of students in your history class.

5. An administrator surveys a random sample of 48 out of 900 middle school students. Using the survey results, the administrator estimates that 225 students are in favor of the new dress code. How many of the 48 students surveyed were in favor of the new dress code?

6. The table show the results of a survey of 75 randomly chosen seventh graders from your school. There are 300 seventh graders in your school. In the survey, each individual was asked to name his or her favorite type of music.

Music	Frequency
Rock	20
Country	23
Rap	30
Classical	2

    a. Estimate the number of seventh graders in your school whose favorite type of music is country.

    b. If you were to repeat the survey using randomly chosen adults, would you predict that the results of the adult survey will be different if you surveyed adults in their 30s versus adults in their 70s? Explain your reasoning.

8.2 Using Random Samples to Describe Populations
For use with Exploration 8.2

Learning Target: Understand variability in samples of a population.

Success Criteria:
- I can use multiple random samples to make conclusions about a population.
- I can use multiple random samples to examine variation in estimates.

1 EXPLORATION: Exploring Variability in Samples

Work with a partner. Sixty percent of all seventh graders have visited a planetarium.

a. Design a simulation using packing peanuts. Mark 60% of the packing peanuts and put them in a paper bag. What does choosing a marked peanut represent?

b. Simulate a sample of 25 students by choosing peanuts from the bag, replacing the peanut each time. Record the results.

8.2 **Using Random Samples to Describe Populations** (continued)

    c. Find the percent of students in the sample who have visited a planetarium. Compare this value to the actual percent of all seventh graders who have visited a planetarium.

    d. Record the percent in part (c) from each pair in the class. Use a dot plot to display the data. Describe the variation in the data.

Name_____ Date_____

8.2 Notetaking with Vocabulary

Vocabulary:

Notes:

8.2 Self-Assessment

Use the scale below to rate your understanding of the learning target and the success criteria.

1	2	3	4
I do not understand.	I can do it with help.	I can do it on my own.	I can teach someone else.

	Rating	Date
8.2 Using Random Samples to Describe Populations		
Learning Target: Understand variability in samples of a population.	1 2 3 4	
I can use multiple random samples to make conclusions about a population.	1 2 3 4	
I can use multiple random samples to examine variation in estimates.	1 2 3 4	

Name _____ Date _____

8.2 Practice

1. Work with a partner. Mark 30 small pieces of paper with an A, a B, or a C. Put the pieces of paper in a bag. Trade bags with other students in the class.

   a. Generate a sample by choosing a piece of paper from your bag 10 times, replacing the piece of paper each time. Record the number of times you choose each letter. Repeat this process to generate five more samples.

   b. Use each sample to make an estimate for the number of As and Bs in the bag. Then describe the variation of the six estimates. Make estimates for the numbers of As, Bs, and Cs in the bag based on all the samples.

   c. Take the pieces of paper out of the bag. How do your estimates compare to the population? Do you think you can make a more accurate estimate? If so, explain how.

2. Work with a partner. You want to know the mean number of hours students in band or orchestra practice their instruments each week. Prior research indicates that the maximum number of hours of practice is 14 hours per week.

   a. Use technology to simulate the hours of practice for 10 students in band or orchestra. Randomly generate 10 numbers from 0 to 14. Write down the results. Repeat the simulation 9 more times, writing down the results each time.

   b. Use each sample to make an estimate for the mean number of hours students in band or orchestra practice their instruments each week. Describe the variation of the estimates.

   c. Use all ten samples to make one estimate for the mean number of hours students in band or orchestra practice their instruments each week. How does your estimate compare to the mean of the entire data set?

   d. Use each sample to make an estimate for the median number of hours students in band or orchestra practice their instruments each week. Describe the variation of the estimates.

   e. Use all ten samples to make one estimate for the median number of hours students in band or orchestra practice their instruments each week.

Name_____ Date _____

Learning Target: Compare populations using measures of center and variation.

Success Criteria:
- I can find the measures of center and variation of a data set.
- I can describe the visual overlap of two data distributions numerically.
- I can determine whether there is a significant difference in the measures of center of two data sets.

1 **EXPLORATION:** Comparing Two Data Distributions

Work with a partner.

a. Does each data display show *overlap*? Explain.

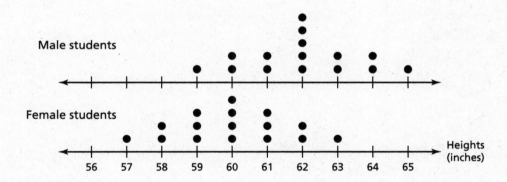

8.3 **Comparing Populations** (continued)

Ages of People in Two Exercise Classes

10:00 A.M. Class							8:00 P.M. Class					
						1	8	9				
						2	1	2	2	7	9	9
						3	0	3	4	5	7	
9	7	3	2	2	2	4	0					
	7	5	4	3	1	5						
		7	0	0		6						
			0			7						

Key: 2 | 4 | 0 = 42 and 40 years

b. How can you describe the overlap of two data distributions using words? How can you describe the overlap numerically?

c. In which pair of data sets is the difference in the measures of center the most significant? Explain your reasoning.

Name_____ Date _____

8.3 Notetaking with Vocabulary

Vocabulary:

Notes:

8.3 Self-Assessment

Use the scale below to rate your understanding of the learning target and the success criteria.

1	2	3	4
I do not understand.	I can do it with help.	I can do it on my own.	I can teach someone else.

	Rating	Date
8.3 Comparing Populations		
Learning Target: Compare populations using measures of center and variation.	1 2 3 4	
I can find the measures of center and variation of a data set.	1 2 3 4	
I can describe the visual overlap of two data distributions numerically.	1 2 3 4	
I can determine whether there is a significant difference in the measures of center of two data sets.	1 2 3 4	

8.3 Practice

1. A scientist experiments with a new type of corn. The dot plots show the heights of corn stalks in two gardens. Experimental corn was planted in Garden A. Traditional corn was planted in Garden B.

a. Compare the data sets using measures of center and variation.

b. Express the difference in the measures of center as a multiple of the measure of variation.

c. If the experimental corn stalks are significantly taller than the traditional corn, the scientist will repeat the experiment in a field rather than a garden. Should the scientist repeat the experiment in a field? Justify your answer.

2. The double box-and-whisker plot represents the runs scored per game by two softball teams during a 15-game season.

a. Compare the data sets using measures of center and variation.

b. Which data set is more likely to contain a value of 3?

c. Is the number of runs scored per game significantly greater for one team than the other? Explain.

Name_____ Date _____

 Using Random Samples to Compare Populations
For use with Exploration 8.4

Learning Target: Use random samples to compare populations.

Success Criteria: • I can compare random samples using measures of center and variation.
   • I can recognize whether random samples are likely to be representative of a population.
   • I can compare populations using multiple random samples.

1 EXPLORATION: Using Random Samples

Work with a partner. You want to compare the numbers of hours spent on homework each week by male and female students in your state. You take a random sample of 15 male students and 15 female students throughout the state.

Male Students

1.5	3	0	2.5	1
8	2.5	1	3	0
6.5	1	5	0	5

Female Students

4	0	3	1	1
5	1	3	5.5	10
2	0	6	3.5	2

a. Compare the data in each sample.

b. Are the samples likely to be representative of all male and female students in your state? Explain.

8.4 **Using Random Samples to Compare Populations** (continued)

c. You take 100 random samples of 15 male students in your state and 100 random samples of 15 female students in your state and record the median of each sample. The double box-and-whisker plot shows the distributions of the sample medians. Compare the distributions in the double box-and-whisker plot with the distributions of the data in the tables.

d. What can you conclude from the double box-and-whisker plot? Explain.

e. How can you use random samples to make accurate comparisons of two populations?

Notetaking with Vocabulary

Vocabulary:

Notes:

8.4 Self-Assessment

Use the scale below to rate your understanding of the learning target and the success criteria.

1	**2**	**3**	**4**
I do not understand.	I can do it with help.	I can do it on my own.	I can teach someone else.

	Rating	Date
8.4 Using Random Samples to Compare Populations		
Learning Target: Use random samples to compare populations.	1 2 3 4	
I can compare random samples using measures of center and variation.	1 2 3 4	
I can recognize whether random samples are likely to be representative of a population.	1 2 3 4	
I can compare populations using multiple random samples.	1 2 3 4	

8.4 Practice

1. The tables show the numbers of attendees at random pep rallies for football and basketball games at a school during the last 5 years.

Football Pep Rally Attendance

174	175	200	169	178	171
165	187	159	170	184	196
205	231	198	310	152	178

Basketball Pep Rally Attendance

143	178	154	167	204	199
254	147	179	162	189	203
217	214	187	210	288	287

a. Find the mean, median, mode, range, interquartile range, and mean absolute deviation for the samples.

b. When comparing the two samples using measures of center and variation, would you use the mean and the MAD, or the median and the IQR? Explain.

c. Compare the samples.

d. Can you determine which pep rally is more popular?

2. Two manufacturing plants each produce 120 frozen food products. A scientist takes 10 samples of 12 frozen food products from each lab and records the number that pass an inspection. Are the samples likely to be representative of all the frozen food products for each manufacturing plant? If so, which lab has more frozen food products that will pass the inspection? Justify your answer.

Manufacturing Plant A

9	8	12	7	9
10	7	11	8	9

Manufacturing Plant B

12	11	11	10	12
12	10	11	12	12

Name_____ Date_____

Chapter 8 Chapter Self-Assessment

Use the scale below to rate your understanding of the learning target and the success criteria.

1	2	3	4
I do not understand.	I can do it with help.	I can do it on my own.	I can teach someone else.

	Rating	Date
8.1 Samples and Populations		
Learning Target: Understand how to use random samples to make conclusions about a population.	1 2 3 4	
I can explain why a sample is biased or unbiased.	1 2 3 4	
I can explain why conclusions made from a biased sample may not be valid.	1 2 3 4	
I can use an unbiased sample to make a conclusion about a population.	1 2 3 4	
8.2 Using Random Samples to Describe Populations		
Learning Target: Understand variability in samples of a population.	1 2 3 4	
I can use multiple random samples to make conclusions about a population.	1 2 3 4	
I can use multiple random samples to examine variation in estimates.	1 2 3 4	
8.3 Comparing Populations		
Learning Target: Compare populations using measures of center and variation.	1 2 3 4	
I can find the measures of center and variation of a data set.	1 2 3 4	
I can describe the visual overlap of two data distributions numerically.	1 2 3 4	
I can determine whether there is a significant difference in the measures of center of two data sets.	1 2 3 4	

Chapter Self-Assessment (continued)

	Rating	Date
8.4 Using Random Samples to Compare Populations		
Learning Target: Use random samples to compare populations.	1 2 3 4	
I can compare random samples using measures of center and variation.	1 2 3 4	
I can recognize whether random samples are likely to be representative of a population.	1 2 3 4	
I can compare populations using multiple random samples.	1 2 3 4	

Name_____ Date_____

Identify the basic shapes in the figure.

1.

2.

3.

4.

5. Identify the basic shapes that make up the top of the teacher's desk.

Chapter 9 **Review & Refresh** (continued)

Use a protractor to find the measure of the angle. Then classify the angle as *acute*, *obtuse*, *right*, or *straight*.

6.

7.

8.

9.

Use a protractor to draw an angle with the given measure.

10. 80°

11. 175°

Name_____ Date_____

9.1 Circles and Circumference
For use with Exploration 9.1

Learning Target: Find the circumference of a circle.

Success Criteria:
- I can explain the relationship between the diameter and circumference of a circle.
- I can use a formula to find the circumference of a circle.

1 EXPLORATION: Using a Compass to Draw a Circle

Work with a partner. Set a compass to 2 inches and draw a circle.

a. Draw a line from one side of the circle to the other that passes through the center. What is the length of the line? This is called the *diameter* of the circle.

b. Estimate the distance around the circle. This is called the *circumference* of the circle. Explain how you found your answer.

9.1 **Circles and Circumference** (continued)

---

2 **EXPLORATION:** Exploring Diameter and Circumference

Work with a partner.

   a. Roll a cylindrical object on a flat surface to find the circumference of the circular base.

   b. Measure the diameter of the circular base. Which is greater, the diameter or the circumference? how many times greater?

   c. Compare your answers in part (b) with the rest of the class. What do you notice?

   d. Without measuring, how can you find the circumference of a circle with a given diameter? Use your method to estimate the circumference of the circle in Exploration 1.

Name_____ Date_____

 9.1 **Notetaking with Vocabulary**

Vocabulary:

Notes:

9.1 **Self-Assessment**

Use the scale below to rate your understanding of the learning target and the success criteria.

1	*2*	*3*	*4*
I do not understand.	I can do it with help.	I can do it on my own.	I can teach someone else.

	Rating	Date
9.1 Circles and Circumference		
Learning Target: Find the circumference of a circle.	1 2 3 4	
I can explain the relationship between the diameter and circumference of a circle.	1 2 3 4	
I can use a formula to find the circumference of a circle.	1 2 3 4	

Name _____   Date _____

9.1   Practice

Find the circumference of the circle. Use 3.14 or $\frac{22}{7}$ for π.

1.
26 m

2.
6 ft

3.
42 in.

Find the perimeter of the semicircular region.

4.
28 yd

5.
7.5 ft

6.
11 cm

7. Consider the circles A, B, C, and D.

A
2.5 ft

B
24 in.

C
32 ft

D
84 in.

    a. Without calculating, which circle has the greatest circumference? Explain.

    b. Without calculating, which circle has the least circumference? Explain.

    c. Find the circumference of each circle in feet. How many times larger is the greatest circumference than the least circumference? How could you find this answer without calculating?

8. A coaster has a circumference of 12.56 inches. Suppose the same amount of coaster is visible around the bottom of a glass as shown. What is the circumference of the glass?

0.5 in.   0.5 in.

9. Are the side lengths of the squares in Diagram A and Diagram B equivalent? Explain your reasoning.

Diagram A   Diagram B

10 ft
1 ft

10. You release a ball with a radius of 1 inch into a pipe as shown. How many times will the ball rotate before it falls out of the other end of the pipe?

1 in.
5 ft

Not drawn to scale

Name _____ Date _____

9.2 Areas of Circles
For use with Exploration 9.2

Learning Target: Find the area of a circle.

Success Criteria:
- I can estimate the area of a circle.
- I can use a formula to find the area of a circle.

---

1 EXPLORATION: Estimating the Area of a Circle

Work with a partner. Each grid contains a circle with a diameter of 4 centimeters. Use each grid to estimate the area of the circle. Which estimate should be closest to the actual area? Explain.

  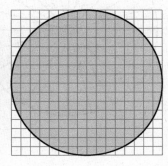

9.2 **Areas of Circles** (continued)

2 EXPLORATION: Writing a Formula for the Area of a Circle

**Work with a partner. A student draws a circle with radius *r* and divides the
circle into 24 equal sections. The student cuts out each section and arranges the
sections to form a shape that resembles a parallelogram.**

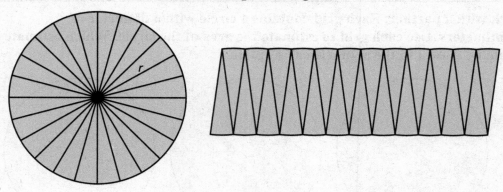

a. Use the diagram to write a formula for the area *A* of a circle in terms of the
radius *r*. Explain your reasoning.

b. Use the formula to check your estimates in Exploration 1.

9.2 Notetaking with Vocabulary

Vocabulary:

Notes:

9.2 Self-Assessment

Use the scale below to rate your understanding of the learning target and the success criteria.

1	**2**	**3**	**4**
I do not understand.	I can do it with help.	I can do it on my own.	I can teach someone else.

	Rating	Date
9.2 Areas of Circles		
Learning Target: Find the area of a circle.	1 2 3 4	
I can estimate the area of a circle.	1 2 3 4	
I can use a formula to find the area of a circle.	1 2 3 4	

Name _____ Date _____

9.2 Practice

Find the area of the circle. Use 3.14 or $\frac{22}{7}$ for π.

1.
35 in.

2.
2.5 m

3.
48 mm

Find the area of the semicircle.

4.
20 in.

5.
16 m

6.
21 ft

7. The shadow of an object is roughly the same size as the object. What is the area of the circular shadow of the hot air balloon?

⊢56 ft⊣

8. How many *square feet* of the ground are sprayed by the beach shower?

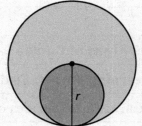
72 in.

9. The radius of the small circle is half the radius of the large circle.

   a. Use the radius r to write a formula for the area of the large circle.

   b. Use the radius $\frac{r}{2}$ to write a formula for the area of the small circle.

   c. How does the area of a circle compare to the area of another circle whose radius is twice as large? Explain your reasoning.

r

10. The number of square inches of a circle's area is equal to the number of inches of its circumference. What is the radius of the circle? Explain how you found your answer.

9.3 Perimeters and Areas of Composite Figures
For use with Exploration 9.3

Learning Target: Find perimeters and areas of composite figures.

Success Criteria:
- I can use a grid to estimate perimeters and areas.
- I can identify the shapes that make up a composite figure.
- I can find the perimeters and areas of shapes that make up composite figures.

1 EXPLORATION: Submitting a Bid

Work with a partner. You want to bid on a project for the pool shown. The project involves ordering and installing the brown tile that borders the pool, and ordering a custom-made tarp to cover the surface of the pool. In the figure, each grid square represents 1 square foot.

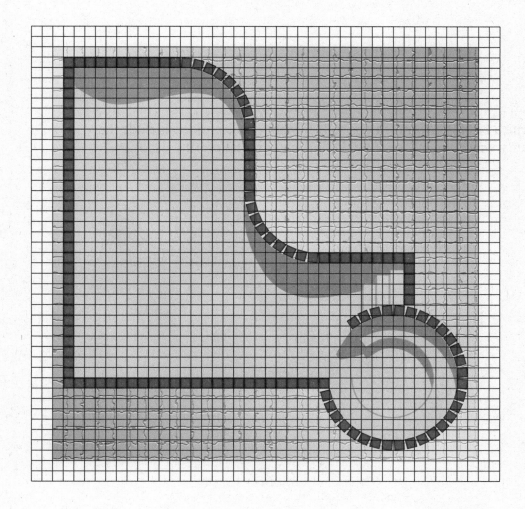

9.3 **Perimeters and Areas of Composite Figures** (continued)

- **You pay \$5 per linear foot for the tile.**

- **You pay \$4 per square foot for the tarp.**

- **It takes you about 15 minutes to install each foot of tile.**

a. Estimate the total cost for the tile and the tarp.

b. Write a bid for how much you will charge for the project. Include the hourly wage you will receive. Estimate your total profit.

9.3 Notetaking with Vocabulary

Vocabulary:

Notes:

9.3 Self-Assessment

Use the scale below to rate your understanding of the learning target and the success criteria.

1	**2**	**3**	**4**
I do not understand.	I can do it with help.	I can do it on my own.	I can teach someone else.

	Rating	Date
9.3 Perimeters and Areas of Composite Figures		
Learning Target: Find perimeters and areas of composite figures.	1 2 3 4	
I can use a grid to estimate perimeters and areas.	1 2 3 4	
I can identify the shapes that make up a composite figure.	1 2 3 4	
I can find the perimeters and areas of shapes that make up composite figures.	1 2 3 4	

Name _____ Date _____

Estimate the perimeter and the area of the shaded figure.

1.

2.

3.
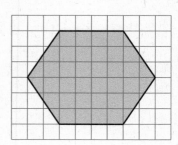

Find the perimeter and the area of the figure.

4.

5.

6.
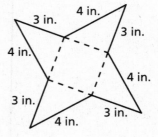

7. Describe and correct the error in finding the perimeter of the figure.

> $\times$ Perimeter $\approx 2 + 7 + 2 + 21.98$
> $= 32.98$ ft

8. A shrub has been cut and trimmed into the shape of an "F". The owner has hired a landscaper to decrease the perimeter of the shrub by 10 feet. Draw a diagram of how the landscaper might do this. Is there more than one way? Explain.

9. A school has a garden in the shape of a pencil. A fence is to be built around the garden. The fence costs $2.75 per foot. How much will it cost to install the fence?

9.4 Constructing Polygons
For use with Exploration 9.4

Learning Target: Construct a polygon with given measures.

Success Criteria:
- I can use technology to draw polygons.
- I can determine whether given measures result in one triangle, many triangles, or no triangle.
- I can draw polygons given angle measures or side lengths.

---

1 **EXPLORATION:** Using Technology to Draw Polygons

Work with a partner.

a. Use geometry software to draw each polygon with the given side lengths or angle measures, if possible. Complete the table.

Side Lengths or Angle Measures	How many figures are possible?
i. 4 cm, 6 cm, 7 cm	
ii. 2 cm, 6 cm, 7 cm	
iii. 2 cm, 4 cm, 7 cm	
iv. 2 cm, 4 cm, 6 cm	
v. 2 in., 3 in., 3 in., 6 in.	
vi. 1 in., 1 in., 3 in., 6 in.	
vii. 1 in., 1 in., 3 in., 4 in.	
viii. 90°, 60°, 30°	
ix. 100°, 40°, 20°	
x. 50°, 60°, 70°	
xi. 20°, 80°, 100°	
xii. 20°, 50°, 50°, 60°	
xiii. 30°, 80°, 120°, 130°	
xiv. 60°, 60°, 120°, 120°	

9.4 **Constructing Polygons** (continued)

b. Without constructing, how can you tell whether it is possible to draw a triangle given three angle measures? three side lengths? Explain your reasoning.

c. Without constructing, how can you tell whether it is possible to draw a quadrilateral given four angle measures? four side lengths? Explain your reasoning.

Name_____ Date _____

9.4 Notetaking with Vocabulary

Vocabulary:

Notes:

9.4 Self-Assessment

Use the scale below to rate your understanding of the learning target and the success criteria.

1	**2**	**3**	**4**
I do not understand.	I can do it with help.	I can do it on my own.	I can teach someone else.

	Rating	Date
9.4 Constructing Polygons		
Learning Target: Construct a polygon with given measures.	1 2 3 4	
I can use technology to draw polygons.	1 2 3 4	
I can determine whether given measures result in one triangle, many triangles, or no triangle.	1 2 3 4	
I can draw polygons given angle measures or side lengths.	1 2 3 4	

9.4 Practice

Draw a triangle with the given angle measures, if possible.

1. 25°, 65°, 90°   **2.** 45°, 60°, 75°

3. Draw a triangle with the given description: a 110° angle connects to a 25° angle by a side of length 6 inches.

Determine whether you can construct *one*, *many*, or *no* triangle(s) with the given description. Explain your reasoning.

4. a triangle with a side length of 2 inches, a side length of 4 inches, and a side length of 5 inches

5. a scalene triangle with two side lengths of 7 centimeters

6. a triangle with one angle measure of 100° and one side length of 6 inches

7. Determine whether the statement is *true* or *false*. Explain your reasoning. You may use diagrams to explain your reasoning.

   a. A rectangle with side lengths of 30 inches and 10 inches can be divided into two congruent squares.

   b. A rectangle with side lengths of 30 inches and 10 inches can be divided into three congruent squares.

   c. A parallelogram with opposite congruent side lengths of 6 feet and 3 feet can be divided into two congruent rhombuses.

   d. A rectangle with side lengths of 30 inches and 10 inches can be divided into two congruent trapezoids.

   e. A rhombus that has side lengths of 8 meters can be divided into two congruent parallelograms.

Construct a quadrilateral with the given description.

8. a kite with side lengths of 2 feet and 5 feet

9. a trapezoid with a base of length 4 meters and an opposite parallel side of length 1 meter

10. a rhombus with adjacent angles of 70° and 110°.

Name_____ Date _____

9.5 Finding Unknown Angle Measures
For use with Exploration 9.5

Learning Target: Use facts about angle relationships to find unknown angle measures.

Success Criteria:
- I can identify adjacent, complementary, supplementary, and vertical angles.
- I can use equations to find unknown angle measures.
- I can find unknown angle measures in real-life situations.

1 EXPLORATION: Using Rules About Angles

Work with a partner. The diagram shows pairs of *adjacent* angles and *vertical* angles. Vertical angles cannot be adjacent.

a. Which pair(s) of angles are adjacent angles? Explain.

b. Which pair(s) of angles are vertical angles? Explain.

c. Without using a protractor, find the values of *x*, *y*, and *z*. Explain your reasoning.

9.5 **Finding Unknown Angle Measures** (continued)

    d. Make a conjecture about the measures of any two vertical angles.

    e. Test your conjecture in part (d) using the diagram below. Explain why your conjecture is or is *not* true.

Name_____ Date _____

 9.5 **Notetaking with Vocabulary**

Vocabulary:

Notes:

9.5 **Self-Assessment**

Use the scale below to rate your understanding of the learning target and the success criteria.

1	**2**	**3**	**4**
I do not understand.	I can do it with help.	I can do it on my own.	I can teach someone else.

	Rating				Date
9.5 Finding Unknown Angle Measures					
Learning Target: Use facts about angle relationships to find unknown angle measures.	1	2	3	4	
I can identify adjacent, complementary, supplementary, and vertical angles.	1	2	3	4	
I can use equations to find unknown angle measures.	1	2	3	4	
I can find unknown angle measures in real-life situations.	1	2	3	4	

9.5 Practice

Name two pairs of adjacent angles and two pairs of vertical angles in the figure.

1.

2.

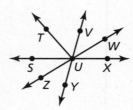

Classify the pair of angles. Then find the value of x.

3.

4.

5.

6.

7. Draw a figure in which $\angle 2$ and $\angle 3$ are acute vertical angles, $\angle 1$ and $\angle 2$ are supplementary angles, $\angle 2$ and $\angle 5$ are complementary angles, and $\angle 4$ and $\angle 5$ are adjacent angles.

8. Find the values of x and y.

9. The measures of two adjacent angles have a ratio of 3 : 5. The sum of the measures of the two adjacent angles is 120°. What is the measure of the larger angle?

10. Let x be an angle measure. Let c be the measure of the complement of the angle and let s be the measure of the supplement of the angle.

    a. Write an equation involving c and x.

    b. Write an equation involving s and x.

Name_____ Date _____

Chapter 9 Chapter Self-Assessment

Use the scale below to rate your understanding of the learning target and the success criteria.

1	2	3	4
I do not understand.	I can do it with help.	I can do it on my own.	I can teach someone else.

	Rating	Date
9.1 Circles and Circumference		
Learning Target: Find the circumference of a circle.	1 2 3 4	
I can explain the relationship between the diameter and circumference of a circle.	1 2 3 4	
I can use a formula to find the circumference of a circle.	1 2 3 4	
9.2 Areas of Circles		
Learning Target: Find the area of a circle.	1 2 3 4	
I can estimate the area of a circle.	1 2 3 4	
I can use a formula to find the area of a circle.	1 2 3 4	
9.3 Perimeters and Areas of Composite Figures		
Learning Target: Find perimeters and areas of composite figures.	1 2 3 4	
I can use a grid to estimate perimeters and areas.	1 2 3 4	
I can identify the shapes that make up a composite figure.	1 2 3 4	
I can find the perimeters and areas of shapes that make up composite figures.	1 2 3 4	

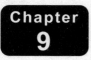

Chapter Self-Assessment (continued)

	Rating	Date
9.4 Constructing Polygons		
Learning Target: Construct a polygon with given measures.	1 2 3 4	
I can use technology to draw polygons.	1 2 3 4	
I can determine whether given measures result in one triangle, many triangles, or no triangle.	1 2 3 4	
I can draw polygons given angle measures or side lengths.	1 2 3 4	
9.5 Finding Unknown Angle Measures		
Learning Target: Use facts about angle relationships to find unknown angle measures.	1 2 3 4	
I can identify adjacent, complementary, supplementary, and vertical angles.	1 2 3 4	
I can use equations to find unknown angle measures.	1 2 3 4	
I can find unknown angle measures in real-life situations.	1 2 3 4	

Chapter 10 Review & Refresh

Find the area of the square or rectangle.

1.

   8 cm
   8 cm

2.

   7 yd
   12 yd

3.

   9.2 in.
   6.4 in.

4.

   $\frac{5}{6}$ m
   $\frac{5}{6}$ m

5.

   $1\frac{1}{3}$ mm
   $2\frac{1}{3}$ mm

6.

   21.3 ft
   15.1 ft

7. An artist buys a square canvas with a side length of 2.5 feet. What is the area of the canvas?

Review & Refresh (continued)

Find the area of the triangle.

8.

4 cm

10 cm

9.

8 ft

3 ft

10.

7 m

6 m

11.

12 yd

5 yd

12.

5 in.

4 in.

13.

9 mm

2 mm

14. A spirit banner for a pep rally has the shape of a triangle. The base of the banner is 8 feet and the height is 6 feet. Find the area of the banner.

10.1 Surface Areas of Prisms
For use with Exploration 10.1

Learning Target: Find the surface area of a prism.

Success Criteria:
- I can use a formula to find the surface area of a prism.
- I can find the lateral surface area of a prism.

1 EXPLORATION: Writing a Formula for Surface Area

Work with a partner.

a. Use the diagrams to write a formula for the surface area of a rectangular prism. Explain your reasoning.

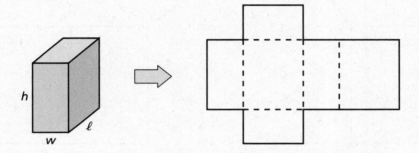

b. Choose dimensions for a rectangular prism. Then draw the prism and use your formula in part (a) to find the surface area.

10.1 **Surface Areas of Prisms** (continued)

2 **EXPLORATION: Surface Area of Prisms**

Work with a partner.

a. Identify the solid represented by the net. Then find the surface area of the solid.

b. Describe a method for finding the surface area of a prism.

10.1 Notetaking with Vocabulary

Vocabulary:

Notes:

10.1 Self-Assessment

Use the scale below to rate your understanding of the learning target and the success criteria.

1	**2**	**3**	**4**
I do not understand.	I can do it with help.	I can do it on my own.	I can teach someone else.

	Rating	Date
10.1 Surface Areas of Prisms		
Learning Target: Find the surface area of a prism.	1 2 3 4	
I can use a formula to find the surface area of a prism.	1 2 3 4	
I can find the lateral surface area of a prism.	1 2 3 4	

10.1 Practice

Find the surface area of the prism.

1.

10 cm
30 cm
24 cm

2.

4 ft
3 ft
8 ft

3.

2 in.
12 in.
2 in.
2.8 in.

4.

14 m
28 m
14 m
10 m
20 m

5.

18 cm
10 cm
10 cm
4 cm
34 cm
6 cm

6.

6 ft
16 ft
6 ft

7. A graphing calculator is in the approximate shape of a rectangular prism.

9 cm
2.5 cm
19 cm

   a. Estimate the total surface area of the calculator.

   b. The window of the calculator is 6.5 centimeters long and 4.5 centimeters wide. Estimate the surface area of the graphing calculator without the window.

8. The least amount of wrapping paper needed to wrap a cube-shaped gift is 150 square inches. How long is one side of the gift?

10.2 Surface Areas of Cylinders
For use with Exploration 10.2

Learning Target: Find the surface area of a cylinder.

Success Criteria:
- I can use a formula to find the surface area of a cylinder.
- I can find the lateral surface area of a cylinder.

---

1 EXPLORATION: Finding the Surface Area of a Cylinder

Work with a partner.

a. Make a net for a can. Name each shape in the net.

b. How are the dimensions of the paper related to the dimensions of the can?

10.2 Surface Areas of Cylinders (continued)

   c. Write a formula that represents the surface area of a cylinder with a height of h and bases with a radius of r.

   d. Estimate the dimensions of a can of tuna and a can of soup. Then use your formula in part (c) to estimate the surface area of each can.

10.2 Notetaking with Vocabulary

Vocabulary:

Notes:

10.2 Self-Assessment

Use the scale below to rate your understanding of the learning target and the success criteria.

1	2	3	4
I do not understand.	I can do it with help.	I can do it on my own.	I can teach someone else.

	Rating	Date
10.2 Surface Areas of Cylinders		
Learning Target: Find the surface area of a cylinder.	1 2 3 4	
I can use a formula to find the surface area of a cylinder.	1 2 3 4	
I can find the lateral surface area of a cylinder.	1 2 3 4	

10.2 Practice

Find the surface area of the cylinder. Round your answer to the nearest tenth if necessary.

1.

12 ft

5 ft

2.

1 cm

9 cm

Find the lateral surface area of the cylinder. Round your answer to the nearest tenth if necessary.

3.

13 m

10 m

4.

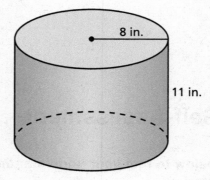

8 in.

11 in.

5. A quarter is worth $0.25 and a half dollar is worth $0.50.

   a. A quarter has a diameter of $\frac{15}{16}$ inch and a height of $\frac{1}{16}$ inch. Find the surface area of a quarter. Round your answer to the nearest hundredth.

   b. A half dollar has a diameter of $\frac{9}{8}$ inches and a height of $\frac{3}{32}$ inch. Find the surface area of a half dollar. Round your answer to the nearest hundredth.

   c. Show that the value of the coin is not proportional to the surface area of the coin.

   d. If the values of the coins were proportional to the surface areas of the coins, what would be the surface area of the half dollar? Round your answer to the nearest hundredth.

10.3 Surface Areas of Pyramids
For use with Exploration 10.3

Learning Target: Find the surface area of a pyramid.

Success Criteria:
- I can use a net to find the surface area of a regular pyramid.
- I can find the lateral surface area of a regular pyramid.

1 EXPLORATION: Making a Scale Model

Work with a partner. Each pyramid listed below has a square base.

Cheops Pyramid in Egypt

Side ≈ 230 m, Slant height ≈ 186 m

Louvre Pyramid in Paris

Side ≈ 35 m, Slant height ≈ 28 m

a. Draw a net for a scale model of one of the pyramids. Describe the scale factor.

10.3 **Surface Areas of Pyramids** (continued)

b. Find the lateral surface area of the real-life pyramid that you chose in part (a). Explain how you found your answer.

c. Draw a net for a pyramid with a non-rectangular base and find its lateral surface area. Explain how you found your answer.

10.3 Notetaking with Vocabulary

Vocabulary:

Notes:

10.3 Self-Assessment

Use the scale below to rate your understanding of the learning target and the success criteria.

1	**2**	**3**	**4**
I do not understand.	I can do it with help.	I can do it on my own.	I can teach someone else.

	Rating	**Date**
10.3 Surface Areas of Pyramids		
Learning Target: Find the surface area of a pyramid.	1 2 3 4	
I can use a net to find the surface area of a regular pyramid.	1 2 3 4	
I can find the lateral surface area of a regular pyramid.	1 2 3 4	

10.3 Practice

Find the surface area of the regular pyramid.

1.

4.3 cm

4.3 cm   6 cm

2.

21 ft

14 ft

14 ft   12.1 ft

3. Researchers have determined that a hip roof offers the most protection to a house during a hurricane.

   a. The house has a square base with a side length of 50 feet. The house has a variation of a hip roof in the shape of a regular pyramid with a square base. The roof extends 1 foot beyond the walls of the house on all sides. What is the length of each side of the base of the roof?

   b. The slant height of the roof is 35 feet. Find the sum of the areas of the lateral faces of the pyramid.

   c. A metal roof covering offers the most protection to a house during a hurricane. The cost of installing metal roof covering is $350 for every 100 square feet of roof. What is the cost of installing a metal roof covering on the house?

4. The surface area of a regular triangular pyramid is 197.1 square meters. The slant height is 12 meters. The area of the base if 35.1 square meters. The base length is 9 meters. What is the height of the triangular base?

5. The surface area of a regular pentagonal pyramid is 125 square yards. The base length is 5 yards. The area of the base is 37.5 square yards. What is the slant height of the pyramid?

Name_____ Date _____

10.4 Volumes of Prisms
For use with Exploration 10.4

Learning Target: Find the volume of a prism.

Success Criteria:
- I can use a formula to find the volume of a prism.
- I can use the formula for the volume of a prism to find a missing dimension.

---

1 EXPLORATION: Finding a Formula for Volume

Work with a partner.

a. In the figures shown, each cube has a volume of 1 cubic unit. Compare the volume V (in cubic units) of each rectangular prism to the area B (in square units) of its base. What do you notice?

10.4 **Volumes of Prisms** (continued)

b. Repeat part (a) using the prisms below.

c. Use what you learned in parts (a) and (b) to write a formula that gives the volume of any prism.

10.4 Notetaking with Vocabulary

Vocabulary:

Notes:

10.4 Self-Assessment

Use the scale below to rate your understanding of the learning target and the success criteria.

1	**2**	**3**	**4**
I do not understand.	I can do it with help.	I can do it on my own.	I can teach someone else.

	Rating	Date
10.4 Volumes of Prisms		
Learning Target: Find the volume of a prism.	1 2 3 4	
I can use a formula to find the volume of a prism.	1 2 3 4	
I can use the formula for the volume of a prism to find a missing dimension.	1 2 3 4	

Name _____   Date _____

10.4 Practice

Find the volume of the prism.

1. 10 cm
20 cm
60 cm

2. 10 m
15 m
25 m

3. A triangular prism has the measurements as shown.

   a. Find the volume of the prism.

   1.2 yd   6 yd   3 yd

   b. Find the volume of the triangular prism if the height of the triangular base is divided by 2.

   c. Explain the relationship between the volume in part (a) and the volume in part (b).

   d. Find the volume of the triangular prism if the height of the prism is divided by 2.

   e. Is the relationship between the volume in part (a) and the volume in part (d) the same as the relationship between the volume in part (a) and the volume in part (b)? Explain.

4. A water tank has the measurements shown. It is 30% full. How many gallons of water are needed to fill the water tank? ($100 \text{ gal} = 0.37854 \text{ m}^3$)

$B = 86 \text{ m}^2$ 15 m

5. A mailbox is in the shape of a prism. The area of the base is 52 square inches and the height is 18 inches. What is the volume of the mailbox?

6. A chicken broth container is in the shape of a rectangular prism, with a length of 9.5 centimeters, a width of 6 centimeters, and a height of 16.5 centimeters. The container is 90% full. How many liters of chicken broth are in the container? ($1 \text{ L} = 1000 \text{ cm}^3$). Round your answer to the nearest hundredth.

7. How many cubic feet are in a cubic yard? Use a sketch to explain your reasoning.

Name_____ Date _____

10.5 Volumes of Pyramids
For use with Exploration 10.5

Learning Target: Find the volume of a pyramid.

Success Criteria:
- I can use a formula to find the volume of a pyramid.
- I can use the volume of a pyramid to solve a real-life problem.

---

1 EXPLORATION: Finding a Formula for the Volume of a Pyramid

Work with a partner. Draw the two nets on cardboard and cut them out. Fold and tape the nets to form an open cube and an open square pyramid. Both figures should have the same size square base and the same height.

a. Compare the volumes of the figures. What do you notice?

b. Use your observations in part (a) to write a formula for the volume of a pyramid.

10.5 **Volumes of Pyramids** (continued)

c. The rectangular prism below can be cut to form three pyramids. Use your
formula in part (b) to show that the sum of the volumes of the three
pyramids is equal to the volume of the prism.

10.5 Notetaking with Vocabulary

Vocabulary:

Notes:

10.5 Self-Assessment

Use the scale below to rate your understanding of the learning target and the success criteria.

1	2	3	4
I do not understand.	I can do it with help.	I can do it on my own.	I can teach someone else.

	Rating	Date
10.5 Volumes of Pyramids		
Learning Target: Find the volume of a pyramid.	1　2　3　4	
I can use a formula to find the volume of a pyramid.	1　2　3　4	
I can use the volume of a pyramid to solve a real-life problem.	1　2　3　4	

10.5 Practice

Find the volume of the pyramid.

1.

12 mm
15 mm
10 mm

2.

14 ft
5 ft
12 ft

3. An amusement park sells popcorn in pyramid-shaped containers. The park charges $0.50 for each 100 cubic centimeters of popcorn. If you purchase the large container, you receive a 25% discount. What is the price for each container? Explain your reasoning.

Pyramid A

22 cm
15 cm
25 cm

Pyramid B

15 in.
$B = 40$ in.²

4 A pyramid has a rectangular base with length of 15 feet and a width of 8 feet. The height of the pyramid is 10 feet.

   a. Find the volume of the pyramid.

   b. When the pyramid was being built, the original base was dropped and it split in two pieces. Each piece was a triangle with a base of 15 feet and a height of 8 feet. Pyramids were made with these two bases, each with a height of 10 feet. Find the combined volume of the two pyramids.

   c. Is the combined volume *greater than*, *less than*, or the *same as* the volume of the pyramid. Explain your reasoning.

5. A triangular pyramid has a volume of 350 cubic centimeters and a height of 10 centimeters. Find one possible set of dimensions of the base.

10.6 Cross Sections of Three-Dimensional Figures

For use with Exploration 10.6

Learning Target: Describe the cross sections of a solid.

Success Criteria:
- I can explain the meaning of a cross section.
- I can describe cross sections of prisms and pyramids.
- I can describe cross sections of cylinders and cones.

1 EXPLORATION: Describing Cross Sections

Work with a partner. A baker is thinking of different ways to slice zucchini bread that is in the shape of a rectangular prism. The shape that is formed by the cut is called a *cross section*.

Cross section

a. What is the shape of the cross section when the baker slices the bread vertically, as shown above?

b. What is the shape of the cross section when the baker slices the bread horizontally?

10.6 **Cross Sections of Three-Dimensional Figures** (continued)

    c. What is the shape of the cross section when the baker slices off a corner of the bread?

    d. Is it possible to obtain a cross section that is a trapezoid? Explain.

    e. Name at least 3 cross sections that are possible to obtain from a rectangular pyramid. Explain your reasoning.

Name_____ Date _____

10.6 Notetaking with Vocabulary

Vocabulary:

Notes:

10.6 Self-Assessment

Use the scale below to rate your understanding of the learning target and the success criteria.

1	**2**	**3**	**4**
I do not understand.	I can do it with help.	I can do it on my own.	I can teach someone else.

	Rating	Date
10.6 Cross Sections of Three-Dimensional Figures		
Learning Target: Describe the cross sections of a solid.	1 2 3 4	
I can explain the meaning of a cross section.	1 2 3 4	
I can describe cross sections of prisms and pyramids.	1 2 3 4	
I can describe cross sections of cylinders and cones.	1 2 3 4	

10.6 Practice

Describe the intersection of the plane and the solid.

1.

2.

3.

4.

5. Describe the cross section of a plane and a cylinder when the plane is parallel to the base of the cylinder. Draw the solid and the cross section.

6. Describe the cross section of a plane and cone when the plane is perpendicular to the base of the cone and passes through the vertex point of the cone. Draw the solid and the cross section.

Determine whether the given intersection is possible. If so, draw the solid and the cross section.

7. The intersection of a plane and a sphere is a point.

8. The intersection of a plane and a cylinder is a triangle.

9. The intersection of a plane and a cylinder is a rectangle.

10. The intersection of a plane and a triangular pyramid is a square.

Name_____ Date_____

Chapter 10 **Chapter Self-Assessment**

Use the scale below to rate your understanding of the learning target and the success criteria.

1	2	3	4
I do not understand.	I can do it with help.	I can do it on my own.	I can teach someone else.

	Rating	Date
10.1 Surface Areas of Prisms		
Learning Target: Find the surface area of a prism.	1 2 3 4	
I can use a formula to find the surface area of a prism.	1 2 3 4	
I can find the lateral surface area of a prism.	1 2 3 4	
10.2 Surface Areas of Cylinders		
Learning Target: Find the surface area of a cylinder.	1 2 3 4	
I can use a formula to find the surface area of a cylinder.	1 2 3 4	
I can find the lateral surface area of a cylinder.	1 2 3 4	
10.3 Surface Areas of Pyramids		
Learning Target: Find the surface area of a pyramid.	1 2 3 4	
I can use a net to find the surface area of a regular pyramid.	1 2 3 4	
I can find the lateral surface area of a regular pyramid.	1 2 3 4	
10.4 Volumes of Prisms		
Learning Target: Find the volume of a prism.	1 2 3 4	
I can use a formula to find the volume of a prism.	1 2 3 4	
I can use the formula for the volume of a prism to find a missing dimension.	1 2 3 4	

Chapter 10 — Chapter Self-Assessment (continued)

	Rating	Date
10.5 Volumes of Pyramids		
Learning Target: Find the volume of a pyramid.	1 2 3 4	
I can use a formula to find the volume of a pyramid.	1 2 3 4	
I can use the volume of a pyramid to solve a real-life problem.	1 2 3 4	
10.6 Cross Sections of Three-Dimensional Figures		
Learning Target: Describe the cross sections of a solid.	1 2 3 4	
I can explain the meaning of a cross section.	1 2 3 4	
I can describe cross sections of prisms and pyramids.	1 2 3 4	
I can describe cross sections of cylinders and cones.	1 2 3 4	

Photo Credits

111 andrearoad/iStock Unreleased/Getty Images Plus;
162 ©iStockphoto.com/Joe Potato Photo;
163 *top* Meral Hydaverdi/Shutterstock.com,
bottom Warren Goldswain/Shutterstock.com

Cover Image briddy_/iStock/Getty Images Plus

Big Ideas Math: Modeling Real Life Grade 7 **249**
Student Journal

Spinner 1

Spinner 2

*Available at *BigIdeasMath.com*.

*Available at *BigIdeasMath.com.*

*Available at *BigIdeasMath.com*.

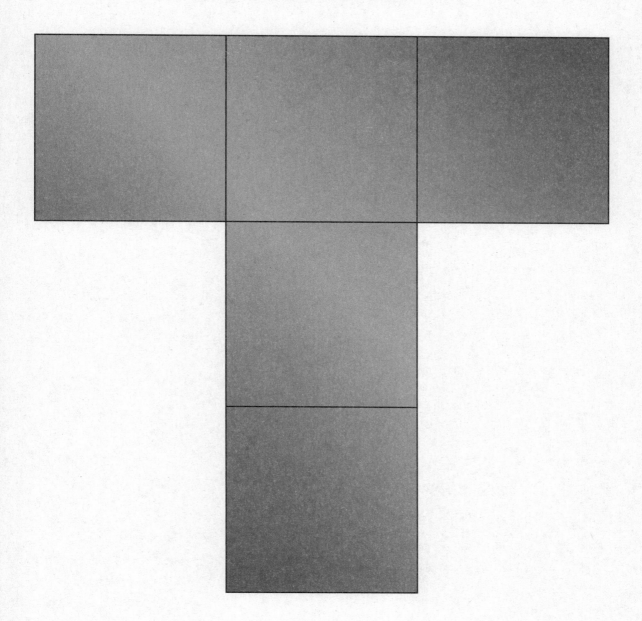

*Available at *BigIdeasMath.com*.

Integer Counters*

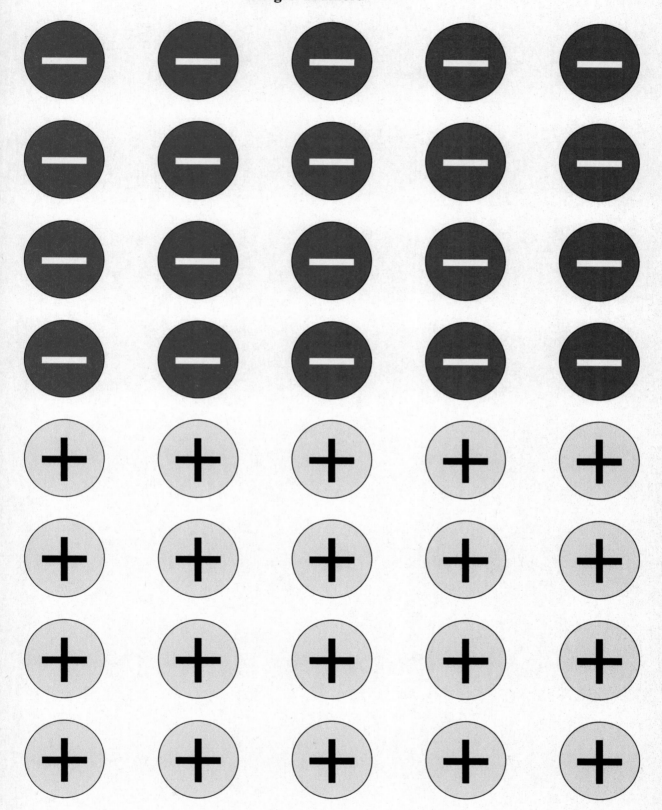

*Available at *BigIdeasMath.com*.

Algebra Tiles*

Algebra Tiles (continued)*

*Available at *BigIdeasMath.com*.